Grace Permitted: A 52-Week Gratitude Journal for
Moms who deserve a bit of Grace.

By: LaTia N. S. Russell , LCSW

Dedication:
This Gratitude Journal is dedicated to a few very special women in my life. In their own ways, they've shown me what it looks like to do this Mom thing, and, I've taken a piece from each of them and have tried my best to walk this path of motherhood with as much Grace & Gratitude as I can. Mom, thank you for always showing up, and for always trying when you physically couldn't. Grandma Martha, thank you for being the matriarch of all matriarchs. You've always given, and continue to give to each of us, just what we need, when we need it. Grandma Freddie Mae, thank you for always showing and making me feel your true unconditional love; but most of all, for being a praying grandmother!

I Love you all infinitely <3!

Grace & Gratitude Belong to:

_____

Grace

Noun

\ gras \
: disposition to or an act or instance of kindness, courtesy, or clemency.

 : a virtue coming from God

: the quality or state of being considerate or thoughtful

Gratitude

Noun

grat•i•tude | \ ˈgra-tə-ˌtüd , -ˌtyüd \

: the state of being grateful.

Introduction

Oh, hi Beautiful Mom, and amazing day to you! I'm so ecstatic that you're here and that you've chosen this journal. I want to take a moment to be completely transparent with you, because I firmly believe transparency is key. I'm a mom, and I've not been very gracious with myself. PHEW! I've literally never said that out loud, and, I think that is in part of what led me to create this gratitude journal.

Let me share a little about myself. I am a Licensed Clinical Social Worker, and have worked in the human services field for over 15 years! Helping people is my passion. I'm also a mom to a very charismatic & energetic 4-year-old son. My family and I reside in an inter-generational household (that's a story & journal for another day). As I'm sure it is with you, with all of the directions I'm pulled in, I can't tell you how many times a day I felt like "The Scream," by Edvard Munch (if you're unfamiliar, google it, and thank me later)!

See, here's the thing, as moms, we often forget to include ourselves when we are extending grace throughout our day, and taking care of everything & everyone around us. In doing that, we tend to forget to take intentional moments for ourselves. These moments are so important to our lives, well-being and the lives & well-being of those around us. When I'm wearing my Social Work hat, all of the tools I share with the people I'm working with roll right off of the tongue. Intuitively, I know the importance of practicing gratitude and being gracious with myself; yet, I still found myself running on fumes. Simply put, I was denying myself the grace needed to keep my tank full.

I realize that we're almost always in mom mode, and finding time to fit one more thing in can be a challenge. So, I've set up this journal with that in mind. The journal has been designed where it should only take a total of 15 minutes per day (about 2-3 minutes for each prompt) to complete an entry. You are provided a space for you to begin your day by setting your intention. As you move through your day, if any readjustments are needed, there is space to complete a quick mid-day check-in. In the evening, you have space to reflect upon your day, & project your intentions for the next day.

Remember, Grace is permitted, and you're entitled to it!

Date: ____ / ____ / ____

Intention:

Today I affirm:...

Three Things That Would Make Today Great:

1) ....

2) ....

3) ....

Must-do's for the day?

....

....

....

Mid-Day Check-In

I am grateful for ....

Reflection

Anything about today that I would change?

....

....

....

Three Amazing things that happened today (big or small)?

1) ....

2) ....

3) ....

Projection

My desires/approach for tomorrow:

....

....

....

Date:____/____/____

Intention:

Today I affirm:..

Three Things That Would Make Today Great:

1) ....

2) ....

3) ....

Must-do's for the day?

....

....

Mid-Day Check-In

I am grateful for..

Reflection

Anything about today that I would change?

....

....

....

Three Amazing things that happened today (big or small)?

1) ....

2) ....

3) ....

Projection

My desires/approach for tomorrow:

....

....

Intention:

Today I affirm:...

Three Things That Would Make Today Great:

1) ....

2) ....

3) ....

Must-do's for the day?

....

....

....

Mid-Day Check-In

I am grateful for ....

Reflection

Anything about today that I would change?

....

....

....

Three Amazing things that happened today (big or small)?

1) ....

2) ....

3) ....

Projection

My desires/approach for tomorrow:

....

....

....

Date: ___/___/___

Intention:

Today I affirm:_____

Three Things That Would Make Today Great:

1) _____

2) _____

3) _____

Must-do's for the day?

_____

_____

Mid-Day Check-In

I am grateful for_____

Reflection

Anything about today that I would change?

_____

_____

_____

Three Amazing things that happened today (big or small)?

1) _____

2) _____

3) _____

Projection

My desires/approach for tomorrow:

_____

_____

Date: ___/___/___

Intention:

Today I affirm:...

Three Things That Would Make Today Great:

1) ....

2) ....

3) ....

Must-do's for the day?

....

....

....

Mid-Day Check-In

I am grateful for ....

Reflection

Anything about today that I would change?

....

....

....

Three Amazing things that happened today (big or small)?

1) ....

2) ....

3) ....

Projection

My desires/approach for tomorrow:

....

....

....

Date:_____/_____/_____

Intention:

Today I affirm:_____

Three Things That Would Make Today Great:

1) ....

2) ....

3) ....

Must-do's for the day?

....

....

....

Mid-Day Check-In

I am grateful for ....

Reflection

Anything about today that I would change?

....

....

....

Three Amazing things that happened today (big or small)?

1) ....

2) ....

3) ....

Projection

My desires/approach for tomorrow:

....

....

....

Date: ___/___/___

Intention:

Today I affirm:...

Three Things That Would Make Today Great:

1) ....

2) ....

3) ....

Must-do's for the day?

....

....

Mid-Day Check-In

I am grateful for ....

Reflection

Anything about today that I would change?

....

....

....

Three Amazing things that happened today (big or small)?

1) ....

2) ....

3) ....

Projection

My desires/approach for tomorrow:

....

....

....

Date: ___ / ___ / ___

Intention:

Today I affirm: ....

Three Things That Would Make Today Great:

1) ....

2) ....

3) ....

Must-do's for the day?

....

....

Mid-Day Check-In

I am grateful for ....

Reflection

Anything about today that I would change?

....

....

Three Amazing things that happened today (big or small)?

1) ....

2) ....

3) ....

Projection

My desires/approach for tomorrow:

....

....

....

Date:_____/_____/_____

Intention:

Today I affirm:...

Three Things That Would Make Today Great:

1) ....

2) ....

3) ....

Must-do's for the day?

....

....

Mid-Day Check-In

I am grateful for ....

Reflection

Anything about today that I would change?

....

....

Three Amazing things that happened today (big or small)?

1) ....

2) ....

3) ....

Projection

My desires/approach for tomorrow:

....

....

Date:_____/_____/_____

Intention:

Today I affirm:_____

Three Things That Would Make Today Great:

1) _____

2) _____

3) _____

Must-do's for the day?

_____

_____

Mid-Day Check-In

I am grateful for_____

Reflection

Anything about today that I would change?

_____

_____

Three Amazing things that happened today (big or small)?

1) _____

2) _____

3) _____

Projection

My desires/approach for tomorrow:

_____

_____

Date:_____/_____/_____

Intention:

Today I affirm:..

Three Things That Would Make Today Great:

1) ....

2) ....

3) ....

Must-do's for the day?

....

....

Mid-Day Check-In

I am grateful for ....

Reflection

Anything about today that I would change?

....

....

Three Amazing things that happened today (big or small)?

1) ....

2) ....

3) ....

Projection

My desires/approach for tomorrow:

....

....

Date:___/___/___

Intention:

Today I affirm:...

Three Things That Would Make Today Great:

1) ....

2) ....

3) ....

Must-do's for the day?

....

....

Mid-Day Check-In

I am grateful for ....

Reflection

Anything about today that I would change?

....

....

....

Three Amazing things that happened today (big or small)?

1) ....

2) ....

3) ....

Projection

My desires/approach for tomorrow:

....

....

....

Date:_____/_____/_____

Intention:

Today I affirm:..

Three Things That Would Make Today Great:

1) ....

2) ....

3) ....

Must-do's for the day?

....

....

....

Mid-Day Check-In

I am grateful for ....

Reflection

Anything about today that I would change?

....

....

....

Three Amazing things that happened today (big or small)?

1) ....

2) ....

3) ....

Projection

My desires/approach for tomorrow:

....

....

....

Date: _____ / _____ / _____

Intention:

Today I affirm: _____

Three Things That Would Make Today Great:

1) _____

2) _____

3) _____

Must-do's for the day?

_____

_____

_____

Mid-Day Check-In

I am grateful for _____

Reflection

Anything about today that I would change?

_____

_____

_____

Three Amazing things that happened today (big or small)?

1) _____

2) _____

3) _____

Projection

My desires/approach for tomorrow:

_____

_____

_____

Date:_____/_____/_____

Intention:

Today I affirm:..

Three Things That Would Make Today Great:

1) ....

2) ....

3) ....

Must-do's for the day?

....

....

Mid-Day Check-In

I am grateful for ....

Reflection

Anything about today that I would change?

....

....

....

Three Amazing things that happened today (big or small)?

1) ....

2) ....

3) ....

Projection

My desires/approach for tomorrow:

....

....

Date: ___/___/___

Intention:

Today I affirm: ....

Three Things That Would Make Today Great:

1) ....

2) ....

3) ....

Must-do's for the day?

....

....

Mid-Day Check-In

I am grateful for ....

Reflection

Anything about today that I would change?

....

....

....

Three Amazing things that happened today (big or small)?

1) ....

2) ....

3) ....

Projection

My desires/approach for tomorrow:

....

....

....

Date: ___/___/___

Intention:

Today I affirm: ....

Three Things That Would Make Today Great:

1) ....

2) ....

3) ....

Must-do's for the day?

....

....

....

Mid-Day Check-In

I am grateful for ....

Reflection

Anything about today that I would change?

....

....

....

Three Amazing things that happened today (big or small)?

1) ....

2) ....

3) ....

Projection

My desires/approach for tomorrow:

....

....

....

Date:_____/_____/_____

Intention:

Today I affirm:_____

Three Things That Would Make Today Great:

1) ....

2) ....

3) ....

Must-do's for the day?

....

....

....

Mid-Day Check-In

I am grateful for ....

Reflection

Anything about today that I would change?

....

....

....

Three Amazing things that happened today (big or small)?

1) ....

2) ....

3) ....

Projection

My desires/approach for tomorrow:

....

....

....

Date: ___ / ___ / ___

Intention:

Today I affirm:...

Three Things That Would Make Today Great:

1) ....

2) ....

3) ....

Must-do's for the day?

....

....

Mid-Day Check-In

I am grateful for ....

Reflection

Anything about today that I would change?

....

....

....

Three Amazing things that happened today (big or small)?

1) ....

2) ....

3) ....

Projection

My desires/approach for tomorrow:

....

....

Date: ___/___/___

Intention:

Today I affirm:_____

Three Things That Would Make Today Great:

1) ....

2) ....

3) ....

Must-do's for the day?

....

....

Mid-Day Check-In

I am grateful for ....

Reflection

Anything about today that I would change?

....

....

....

Three Amazing things that happened today (big or small)?

1) ....

2) ....

3) ....

Projection

My desires/approach for tomorrow:

....

....

....

Date: ___ / ___ / ___

Intention:

Today I affirm: ....

Three Things That Would Make Today Great:

1) ....

2) ....

3) ....

Must-do's for the day?

....

....

....

Mid-Day Check-In

I am grateful for ....

Reflection

Anything about today that I would change?

....

....

....

Three Amazing things that happened today (big or small)?

1) ....

2) ....

3) ....

Projection

My desires/approach for tomorrow:

....

....

....

Date:_____/_____/_____

Intention:

Today I affirm:

Three Things That Would Make Today Great:

1)

2)

3)

Must-do's for the day?

Mid-Day Check-In

I am grateful for

Reflection

Anything about today that I would change?

Three Amazing things that happened today (big or small)?

1)

2)

3)

Projection

My desires/approach for tomorrow:

Date: ___ / ___ / ___

Intention:

Today I affirm: ....

Three Things That Would Make Today Great:

1) ....

2) ....

3) ....

Must-do's for the day?

....

....

Mid-Day Check-In

I am grateful for ....

Reflection

Anything about today that I would change?

....

....

Three Amazing things that happened today (big or small)?

1) ....

2) ....

3) ....

Projection

My desires/approach for tomorrow:

....

....

Date: ___/___/___

Intention:

Today I affirm:..

1) ....

2) ....

3) ....

Must-do's for the day?

....

....

Mid-Day Check-In

I am grateful for ....

Reflection

Anything about today that I would change?

....

....

....

Three Amazing things that happened today (big or small)?

1) ....

2) ....

3) ....

Projection

My desires/approach for tomorrow:

....

....

....

Date: ___/___/___

Intention:

Today I affirm:..

Three Things That Would Make Today Great:

1) ....

2) ....

3) ....

Must-do's for the day?

....

....

Mid-Day Check-In

I am grateful for ....

Reflection

Anything about today that I would change?

....

....

....

Three Amazing things that happened today (big or small)?

1) ....

2) ....

3) ....

Projection

My desires/approach for tomorrow:

....

....

....

Date: ___/___/___

Intention:

Today I affirm:..

Three Things That Would Make Today Great:

1) ....

2) ....

3) ....

Must-do's for the day?

....

....

Mid-Day Check-In

I am grateful for ....

Reflection

Anything about today that I would change?

....

....

Three Amazing things that happened today (big or small)?

1) ....

2) ....

3) ....

Projection

My desires/approach for tomorrow:

....

....

Date: _____ / _____ / _____

Intention:

Today I affirm:..

Three Things That Would Make Today Great:

1) ....

2) ....

3) ....

Must-do's for the day?

....

....

....

Mid-Day Check-In

I am grateful for ....

Reflection

Anything about today that I would change?

....

....

....

Three Amazing things that happened today (big or small)?

1) ....

2) ....

3) ....

Projection

My desires/approach for tomorrow:

....

....

....

Date: ____/____/____

Intention:

Today I affirm: ....

Three Things That Would Make Today Great:

1) ....

2) ....

3) ....

Must-do's for the day?

....

....

Mid-Day Check-In

I am grateful for ....

Reflection

Anything about today that I would change?

....

....

....

Three Amazing things that happened today (big or small)?

1) ....

2) ....

3) ....

Projection

My desires/approach for tomorrow:

....

....

Date: ___/___/___

Intention:

Today I affirm:..

Three Things That Would Make Today Great:

1) ....

2) ....

3) ....

Must-do's for the day?

....

....

....

Mid-Day Check-In

I am grateful for ....

Reflection

Anything about today that I would change?

....

....

....

Three Amazing things that happened today (big or small)?

1) ....

2) ....

3) ....

Projection

My desires/approach for tomorrow:

....

....

Date: ___/___/___

Intention:

Today I affirm:_____

Three Things That Would Make Today Great:

1) _____

2) _____

3) _____

Must-do's for the day?

_____

_____

_____

Mid-Day Check-In

I am grateful for_____

Reflection

Anything about today that I would change?

_____

_____

_____

Three Amazing things that happened today (big or small)?

1) _____

2) _____

3) _____

Projection

My desires/approach for tomorrow:

_____

_____

_____

Date:___/___/___

Intention:

Today I affirm:..

Three Things That Would Make Today Great:

1) ....

2) ....

3) ....

Must-do's for the day?

....

....

....

Mid-Day Check-In

I am grateful for ....

Reflection

Anything about today that I would change?

....

....

....

Three Amazing things that happened today (big or small)?

1) ....

2) ....

3) ....

Projection

My desires/approach for tomorrow:

....

....

....

Date: ____ / ____ / ____

Intention:

Today I affirm:..

Three Things That Would Make Today Great:

1) ....

2) ....

3) ....

Must-do's for the day?

....

....

Mid-Day Check-In

I am grateful for ....

Reflection

Anything about today that I would change?

....

....

....

Three Amazing things that happened today (big or small)?

1) ....

2) ....

3) ....

Projection

My desires/approach for tomorrow:

....

....

Date: ___ / ___ / ___

Intention:

Today I affirm: ....

Three Things That Would Make Today Great:

1) ....

2) ....

3) ....

Must-do's for the day?

....

....

....

Mid-Day Check-In

I am grateful for ....

Reflection

Anything about today that I would change?

....

....

....

Three Amazing things that happened today (big or small)?

1) ....

2) ....

3) ....

Projection

My desires/approach for tomorrow:

....

....

....

Date: ___/___/___

Intention:

Today I affirm:_____

Three Things That Would Make Today Great:

1) _____

2) _____

3) _____

Must-do's for the day?

_____

_____

Mid-Day Check-In

I am grateful for _____

Reflection

Anything about today that I would change?

_____

_____

_____

Three Amazing things that happened today (big or small)?

1) _____

2) _____

3) _____

Projection

My desires/approach for tomorrow:

_____

_____

Date:_____/_____/_____

Intention:

Today I affirm:..

Three Things That Would Make Today Great:

1) ....

2) ....

3) ....

Must-do's for the day?

....

....

....

Mid-Day Check-In

I am grateful for ....

Reflection

Anything about today that I would change?

....

....

....

....

Three Amazing things that happened today (big or small)?

1) ....

2) ....

3) ....

Projection

My desires/approach for tomorrow:

....

....

....

Date:____/____/____

Intention:

Today I affirm:_____

Three Things That Would Make Today Great:

1) ....

2) ....

3) ....

Must-do's for the day?

....

....

....

Mid-Day Check-In

I am grateful for ....

Reflection

Anything about today that I would change?

....

....

....

Three Amazing things that happened today (big or small)?

1) ....

2) ....

3) ....

Projection

My desires/approach for tomorrow:

....

....

....

Date: _____ / _____ / _____

Intention:

Today I affirm: ....

Three Things That Would Make Today Great:

1) ....

2) ....

3) ....

Must-do's for the day?

....

....

Mid-Day Check-In

I am grateful for ....

Reflection

Anything about today that I would change?

....

....

....

Three Amazing things that happened today (big or small)?

1) ....

2) ....

3) ....

Projection

My desires/approach for tomorrow:

....

....

Date: ____ / ____ / ____

Intention:

Today I affirm: ....

Three Things That Would Make Today Great:

1) ....

2) ....

3) ....

Must-do's for the day?

....

....

Mid-Day Check-In

I am grateful for ....

Reflection

Anything about today that I would change?

....

....

....

Three Amazing things that happened today (big or small)?

1) ....

2) ....

3) ....

Projection

My desires/approach for tomorrow:

....

....

Date: ____ / ____ / ____

Intention:

Today I affirm: ....

Three Things That Would Make Today Great:

1) ....

2) ....

3) ....

Must-do's for the day?

....

....

Mid-Day Check-In

I am grateful for ....

Reflection

Anything about today that I would change?

....

....

....

Three Amazing things that happened today (big or small)?

1) ....

2) ....

3) ....

Projection

My desires/approach for tomorrow:

....

....

Date: ___ / ___ / ___

Intention:

Today I affirm: _____

Three Things That Would Make Today Great:

1) _____

2) _____

3) _____

Must-do's for the day?

_____

_____

Mid-Day Check-In

I am grateful for _____

Reflection

Anything about today that I would change?

_____

_____

_____

Three Amazing things that happened today (big or small)?

1) _____

2) _____

3) _____

Projection

My desires/approach for tomorrow:

_____

_____

Date: ___/___/___

Intention:

Today I affirm: ....

Three Things That Would Make Today Great:

1) ....

2) ....

3) ....

Must-do's for the day?

....

....

....

Mid-Day Check-In

I am grateful for ....

Reflection

Anything about today that I would change?

....

....

....

Three Amazing things that happened today (big or small)?

1) ....

2) ....

3) ....

Projection

My desires/approach for tomorrow:

....

....

....

Date: _____ / _____ / _____

Intention:

Today I affirm:_____

Three Things That Would Make Today Great:

1) _____

2) _____

3) _____

Must-do's for the day?

Mid-Day Check-In

I am grateful for _____

Reflection

Anything about today that I would change?

Three Amazing things that happened today (big or small)?

1) _____

2) _____

3) _____

Projection

My desires/approach for tomorrow:

Date: ___/___/___

Intention:

Today I affirm: ....

Three Things That Would Make Today Great:

1) ....

2) ....

3) ....

Must-do's for the day?

....

....

....

Mid-Day Check-In

I am grateful for ....

Reflection

Anything about today that I would change?

....

....

....

Three Amazing things that happened today (big or small)?

1) ....

2) ....

3) ....

Projection

My desires/approach for tomorrow:

....

....

....

Date: ___/___/___

Intention:

Today I affirm: ....

Three Things That Would Make Today Great:

1) ....

2) ....

3) ....

Must-do's for the day?

....

....

Mid-Day Check-In

I am grateful for ....

Reflection

Anything about today that I would change?

....

....

....

Three Amazing things that happened today (big or small)?

1) ....

2) ....

3) ....

Projection

My desires/approach for tomorrow:

....

....

....

Date: ___ / ___ / ___

Intention:

Today I affirm:..

Three Things That Would Make Today Great:

1) ....

2) ....

3) ....

Must-do's for the day?

....

....

Mid-Day Check-In

I am grateful for ....

Reflection

Anything about today that I would change?

....

....

....

Three Amazing things that happened today (big or small)?

1) ....

2) ....

3) ....

Projection

My desires/approach for tomorrow:

....

....

Date: ___ / ___ / ___

Intention:

Today I affirm:...

Three Things That Would Make Today Great:

1) ....

2) ....

3) ....

Must-do's for the day?

....

....

Mid-Day Check-In

I am grateful for ....

Reflection

Anything about today that I would change?

....

....

....

Three Amazing things that happened today (big or small)?

1) ....

2) ....

3) ....

Projection

My desires/approach for tomorrow:

....

....

Date:_____/_____/_____

Intention:

Today I affirm:..

Three Things That Would Make Today Great:

1) ....

2) ....

3) ....

Must-do's for the day?

....

....

Mid-Day Check-In

I am grateful for ....

Reflection

Anything about today that I would change?

....

....

Three Amazing things that happened today (big or small)?

1) ....

2) ....

3) ....

Projection

My desires/approach for tomorrow:

....

....

Date: ___/___/___

Intention:

Today I affirm: ....

Three Things That Would Make Today Great:

1) ....

2) ....

3) ....

Must-do's for the day?

....

....

Mid-Day Check-In

I am grateful for ....

Reflection

Anything about today that I would change?

....

....

....

Three Amazing things that happened today (big or small)?

1) ....

2) ....

3) ....

Projection

My desires/approach for tomorrow:

....

....

Date: ___/___/___

Intention:

Today I affirm: ....

Three Things That Would Make Today Great:

1) ....

2) ....

3) ....

Must-do's for the day?

....

....

....

Mid-Day Check-In

I am grateful for ....

Reflection

Anything about today that I would change?

....

....

....

Three Amazing things that happened today (big or small)?

1) ....

2) ....

3) ....

Projection

My desires/approach for tomorrow:

....

....

....

Date: ___/___/___

Intention:

Today I affirm:_____

Three Things That Would Make Today Great:

1) _____

2) _____

3) _____

Must-do's for the day?

_____

_____

Mid-Day Check-In

I am grateful for_____

Reflection

Anything about today that I would change?

_____

_____

_____

Three Amazing things that happened today (big or small)?

1) _____

2) _____

3) _____

Projection

My desires/approach for tomorrow:

_____

_____

Date: ___ / ___ / ___

Intention:

Today I affirm: ....

Three Things That Would Make Today Great:

1) ....

2) ....

3) ....

Must-do's for the day?

....

....

Mid-Day Check-In

I am grateful for ....

Reflection

Anything about today that I would change?

....

....

....

Three Amazing things that happened today (big or small)?

1) ....

2) ....

3) ....

Projection

My desires/approach for tomorrow:

....

....

Date:_____/_____/_____

Intention:

Today I affirm:_____

Three Things That Would Make Today Great:

1) _____

2) _____

3) _____

Must-do's for the day?

_____

_____

Mid-Day Check-In

I am grateful for _____

Reflection

Anything about today that I would change?

_____

_____

_____

Three Amazing things that happened today (big or small)?

1) _____

2) _____

3) _____

Projection

My desires/approach for tomorrow:

_____

_____

_____

Date: ___/___/___

Intention:

Today I affirm:...

Three Things That Would Make Today Great:

1) ....

2) ....

3) ....

Must-do's for the day?

....

....

....

Mid-Day Check-In

I am grateful for ....

Reflection

Anything about today that I would change?

....

....

....

Three Amazing things that happened today (big or small)?

1) ....

2) ....

3) ....

Projection

My desires/approach for tomorrow:

....

....

Date: ___ / ___ / ___

Intention:

Today I affirm:_____

Three Things That Would Make Today Great:

1) ....

2) ....

3) ....

Must-do's for the day?

....

....

Mid-Day Check-In

I am grateful for ....

Reflection

Anything about today that I would change?

....

....

....

Three Amazing things that happened today (big or small)?

1) ....

2) ....

3) ....

Projection

My desires/approach for tomorrow:

....

....

Date: ___/___/___

Intention:

Today I affirm:..

Three Things That Would Make Today Great:

1) ....

2) ....

3) ....

Must-do's for the day?

....

....

Mid-Day Check-In

I am grateful for ....

Reflection

Anything about today that I would change?

....

....

....

Three Amazing things that happened today (big or small)?

1) ....

2) ....

3) ....

Projection

My desires/approach for tomorrow:

....

....

Date:_____/_____/_____

Intention:

Today I affirm:..

Three Things That Would Make Today Great:

1) ....

2) ....

3) ....

Must-do's for the day?

....

....

Mid-Day Check-In

I am grateful for ....

Reflection

Anything about today that I would change?

....

....

....

Three Amazing things that happened today (big or small)?

1) ....

2) ....

3) ....

Projection

My desires/approach for tomorrow:

....

....

Date:_____/_____/_____

Intention:

Today I affirm:..

Three Things That Would Make Today Great:

1) ....

2) ....

3) ....

Must-do's for the day?

....

....

....

Mid-Day Check-In

I am grateful for ....

Reflection

Anything about today that I would change?

....

....

....

Three Amazing things that happened today (big or small)?

1) ....

2) ....

3) ....

Projection

My desires/approach for tomorrow:

....

....

....

Date: ___/___/___

Intention:

Today I affirm:...

Three Things That Would Make Today Great:

1) ....

2) ....

3) ....

Must-do's for the day?

....

....

Mid-Day Check-In

I am grateful for ....

Reflection

Anything about today that I would change?

....

....

Three Amazing things that happened today (big or small)?

1) ....

2) ....

3) ....

Projection

My desires/approach for tomorrow:

....

....

Date: ___/___/___

Intention:

Today I affirm: ....

Three Things That Would Make Today Great:

1) ....

2) ....

3) ....

Must-do's for the day?

....

....

....

Mid-Day Check-In

I am grateful for ....

Reflection

Anything about today that I would change?

....

....

....

Three Amazing things that happened today (big or small)?

1) ....

2) ....

3) ....

Projection

My desires/approach for tomorrow:

....

....

....

Date: ___ / ___ / ___

Intention:

Today I affirm:

Three Things That Would Make Today Great:

1)

2)

3)

Must-do's for the day?

Mid-Day Check-In

I am grateful for

Reflection

Anything about today that I would change?

Three Amazing things that happened today (big or small)?

1)

2)

3)

Projection

My desires/approach for tomorrow:

Date:_____/_____/_____

Intention:

Today I affirm:..

Three Things That Would Make Today Great:

1) ....

2) ....

3) ....

Must-do's for the day?

....

....

Mid-Day Check-In

I am grateful for ....

Reflection

Anything about today that I would change?

....

....

....

Three Amazing things that happened today (big or small)?

1) ....

2) ....

3) ....

Projection

My desires/approach for tomorrow:

....

....

Date:___/___/___

Intention:

Today I affirm:...

Three Things That Would Make Today Great:

1) ....

2) ....

3) ....

Must-do's for the day?

....

....

Mid-Day Check-In

I am grateful for ....

Reflection

Anything about today that I would change?

....

....

....

Three Amazing things that happened today (big or small)?

1) ....

2) ....

3) ....

Projection

My desires/approach for tomorrow:

....

....

Date: ___ / ___ / ___

Intention:

Today I affirm: ....

Three Things That Would Make Today Great:

1) ....

2) ....

3) ....

Must-do's for the day?

....

....

....

Mid-Day Check-In

I am grateful for ....

Reflection

Anything about today that I would change?

....

....

....

Three Amazing things that happened today (big or small)?

1) ....

2) ....

3) ....

Projection

My desires/approach for tomorrow:

....

....

....

Date:_____/_____/_____

Intention:

Today I affirm:_____

Three Things That Would Make Today Great:

1) _____

2) _____

3) _____

Must-do's for the day?

_____

_____

Mid-Day Check-In

I am grateful for _____

Reflection

Anything about today that I would change?

_____

_____

Three Amazing things that happened today (big or small)?

1) _____

2) _____

3) _____

Projection

My desires/approach for tomorrow:

_____

_____

Date: ___/___/___

Intention:

Today I affirm: ....

Three Things That Would Make Today Great:

1) ....

2) ....

3) ....

Must-do's for the day?

....

....

Mid-Day Check-In

I am grateful for ....

Reflection

Anything about today that I would change?

....

....

Three Amazing things that happened today (big or small)?

1) ....

2) ....

3) ....

Projection

My desires/approach for tomorrow:

....

....

Date:_____/_____/_____

Intention:

Today I affirm:..

Three Things That Would Make Today Great:

1) ....

2) ....

3) ....

Must-do's for the day?

....

....

Mid-Day Check-In

I am grateful for..

Reflection

Anything about today that I would change?

....

....

....

Three Amazing things that happened today (big or small)?

1) ....

2) ....

3) ....

Projection

My desires/approach for tomorrow:

....

....

Date: ___ / ___ / ___

Intention:

Today I affirm: ....

Three Things That Would Make Today Great:

1) ....

2) ....

3) ....

Must-do's for the day?

....

....

Mid-Day Check-In

I am grateful for ....

Reflection

Anything about today that I would change?

....

....

....

Three Amazing things that happened today (big or small)?

1) ....

2) ....

3) ....

Projection

My desires/approach for tomorrow:

....

....

....

Date:___/___/___

Intention:

Today I affirm:...

Three Things That Would Make Today Great:

1) ....

2) ....

3) ....

Must-do's for the day?

....

....

Mid-Day Check-In

I am grateful for...

Reflection

Anything about today that I would change?

....

....

....

Three Amazing things that happened today (big or small)?

1) ....

2) ....

3) ....

Projection

My desires/approach for tomorrow:

....

....

....

Date: ___/___/___

Intention:

Today I affirm:...

Three Things That Would Make Today Great:

1) ....

2) ....

3) ....

Must-do's for the day?

....

....

Mid-Day Check-In

I am grateful for ....

Reflection

Anything about today that I would change?

....

....

....

Three Amazing things that happened today (big or small)?

1) ....

2) ....

3) ....

Projection

My desires/approach for tomorrow:

....

....

....

Date: ___/___/___

Intention:

Today I affirm:..

Three Things That Would Make Today Great:

1) ....

2) ....

3) ....

Must-do's for the day?

....

....

Mid-Day Check-In

I am grateful for ....

Reflection

Anything about today that I would change?

....

....

Three Amazing things that happened today (big or small)?

1) ....

2) ....

3) ....

Projection

My desires/approach for tomorrow:

....

....

Date: ___/___/___

Intention:

Today I affirm:...

Three Things That Would Make Today Great:

1) ....

2) ....

3) ....

Must-do's for the day?

....

....

....

Mid-Day Check-In

I am grateful for ....

Reflection

Anything about today that I would change?

....

....

....

Three Amazing things that happened today (big or small)?

1) ....

2) ....

3) ....

Projection

My desires/approach for tomorrow:

....

....

Date: ___/___/___

Intention:

Today I affirm:_____

Three Things That Would Make Today Great:

1) _____

2) _____

3) _____

Must-do's for the day?

_____

_____

Mid-Day Check-In

I am grateful for _____

Reflection

Anything about today that I would change?

_____

_____

_____

Three Amazing things that happened today (big or small)?

1) _____

2) _____

3) _____

Projection

My desires/approach for tomorrow:

_____

_____

Date: ____/____/____

Intention:

Today I affirm:..

Three Things That Would Make Today Great:

1) ....

2) ....

3) ....

Must-do's for the day?

....

....

Mid-Day Check-In

I am grateful for ....

Reflection

Anything about today that I would change?

....

....

....

Three Amazing things that happened today (big or small)?

1) ....

2) ....

3) ....

Projection

My desires/approach for tomorrow:

....

....

....

Date: ___/___/___

Intention:

Today I affirm:_____

Three Things That Would Make Today Great:

1) ....

2) ....

3) ....

Must-do's for the day?

....

....

....

Mid-Day Check-In

I am grateful for ....

Reflection

Anything about today that I would change?

....

....

....

Three Amazing things that happened today (big or small)?

1) ....

2) ....

3) ....

Projection

My desires/approach for tomorrow:

....

....

....

Date: ___/___/___

Intention:

Today I affirm: ....

Three Things That Would Make Today Great:

1) ....

2) ....

3) ....

Must-do's for the day?

....

....

Mid-Day Check-In

I am grateful for ....

Reflection

Anything about today that I would change?

....

....

....

Three Amazing things that happened today (big or small)?

1) ....

2) ....

3) ....

Projection

My desires/approach for tomorrow:

....

....

....

Date:_____/_____/_____

Intention:

Today I affirm:...

Three Things That Would Make Today Great:

1) ....

2) ....

3) ....

Must-do's for the day?

....

....

Mid-Day Check-In

I am grateful for ....

Reflection

Anything about today that I would change?

....

....

Three Amazing things that happened today (big or small)?

1) ....

2) ....

3) ....

Projection

My desires/approach for tomorrow:

....

....

Date: ___ / ___ / ___

Intention:

Today I affirm:...

Three Things That Would Make Today Great:

1) ....

2) ....

3) ....

Must-do's for the day?

....

....

....

Mid-Day Check-In

I am grateful for ....

Reflection

Anything about today that I would change?

....

....

....

Three Amazing things that happened today (big or small)?

1) ....

2) ....

3) ....

Projection

My desires/approach for tomorrow:

....

....

Date: ___/___/___

Intention:

Today I affirm:...

Three Things That Would Make Today Great:

1) ....

2) ....

3) ....

Must-do's for the day?

....

....

Mid-Day Check-In

I am grateful for ....

Reflection

Anything about today that I would change?

....

....

Three Amazing things that happened today (big or small)?

1) ....

2) ....

3) ....

Projection

My desires/approach for tomorrow:

....

....

Date: ___/___/___

Intention:

Today I affirm: ....

Three Things That Would Make Today Great:

1) ....

2) ....

3) ....

Must-do's for the day?

....

....

Mid-Day Check-In

I am grateful for ....

Reflection

Anything about today that I would change?

....

....

....

Three Amazing things that happened today (big or small)?

1) ....

2) ....

3) ....

Projection

My desires/approach for tomorrow:

....

....

Date:_____/_____/_____

Intention:

Today I affirm:_____

Three Things That Would Make Today Great:

1) _____

2) _____

3) _____

Must-do's for the day?

_____

_____

Mid-Day Check-In

I am grateful for _____

Reflection

Anything about today that I would change?

_____

_____

_____

Three Amazing things that happened today (big or small)?

1) _____

2) _____

3) _____

Projection

My desires/approach for tomorrow:

_____

_____

_____

Date:____/____/____

Intention:

Today I affirm:...

Three Things That Would Make Today Great:

1) ....

2) ....

3) ....

Must-do's for the day?

....

....

Mid-Day Check-In

I am grateful for ....

Reflection

Anything about today that I would change?

....

....

Three Amazing things that happened today (big or small)?

1) ....

2) ....

3) ....

Projection

My desires/approach for tomorrow:

....

....

Date: ___/___/___

Intention:

Today I affirm:_____

Three Things That Would Make Today Great:

1) ....

2) ....

3) ....

Must-do's for the day?

....

....

....

Mid-Day Check-In

I am grateful for ....

Reflection

Anything about today that I would change?

....

....

....

Three Amazing things that happened today (big or small)?

1) ....

2) ....

3) ....

Projection

My desires/approach for tomorrow:

....

....

....

Date: ___/___/___

Intention:

Today I affirm: ....

Three Things That Would Make Today Great:

1) ....

2) ....

3) ....

Must-do's for the day?

....

....

Mid-Day Check-In

I am grateful for ....

Reflection

Anything about today that I would change?

....

....

Three Amazing things that happened today (big or small)?

1) ....

2) ....

3) ....

Projection

My desires/approach for tomorrow:

....

....

Date: ____ / ____ / ____

Intention:

Today I affirm: ....

Three Things That Would Make Today Great:

1) ....

2) ....

3) ....

Must-do's for the day?

....

....

Mid-Day Check-In

I am grateful for ....

Reflection

Anything about today that I would change?

....

....

....

Three Amazing things that happened today (big or small)?

1) ....

2) ....

3) ....

Projection

My desires/approach for tomorrow:

....

....

Date: ___/___/___

Intention:

Today I affirm: ....

Three Things That Would Make Today Great:

1) ....

2) ....

3) ....

Must-do's for the day?

....

....

....

Mid-Day Check-In

I am grateful for ....

Reflection

Anything about today that I would change?

....

....

....

Three Amazing things that happened today (big or small)?

1) ....

2) ....

3) ....

Projection

My desires/approach for tomorrow:

....

....

....

Date:____/____/____

Intention:

Today I affirm:_____

Three Things That Would Make Today Great:

1) _____

2) _____

3) _____

Must-do's for the day?

_____

_____

Mid-Day Check-In

I am grateful for _____

Reflection

Anything about today that I would change?

_____

_____

Three Amazing things that happened today (big or small)?

1) _____

2) _____

3) _____

Projection

My desires/approach for tomorrow:

_____

_____

Date: ___ / ___ / ___

Intention:

Today I affirm:...

Three Things That Would Make Today Great:

1) ....

2) ....

3) ....

Must-do's for the day?

....

....

Mid-Day Check-In

I am grateful for ....

Reflection

Anything about today that I would change?

....

....

....

Three Amazing things that happened today (big or small)?

1) ....

2) ....

3) ....

Projection

My desires/approach for tomorrow:

....

....

Date:___/___/___

Intention:

Today I affirm:...

Three Things That Would Make Today Great:

1) ....

2) ....

3) ....

Must-do's for the day?

....

....

Mid-Day Check-In

I am grateful for..

Reflection

Anything about today that I would change?

....

....

....

Three Amazing things that happened today (big or small)?

1) ....

2) ....

3) ....

Projection

My desires/approach for tomorrow:

....

....

....

Date: ___/___/___

Intention:

Today I affirm:...

Three Things That Would Make Today Great:

1) ....

2) ....

3) ....

Must-do's for the day?

....

....

Mid-Day Check-In

I am grateful for ....

Reflection

Anything about today that I would change?

....

....

....

Three Amazing things that happened today (big or small)?

1) ....

2) ....

3) ....

Projection

My desires/approach for tomorrow:

....

....

Date: ___ / ___ / ___

Intention:

Today I affirm:_____

Three Things That Would Make Today Great:

1) _____

2) _____

3) _____

Must-do's for the day?

_____

_____

Mid-Day Check-In

I am grateful for _____

Reflection

Anything about today that I would change?

_____

_____

Three Amazing things that happened today (big or small)?

1) _____

2) _____

3) _____

Projection

My desires/approach for tomorrow:

_____

_____

Date:___/___/___

Intention:

Today I affirm:..

Three Things That Would Make Today Great:

1) ....

2) ....

3) ....

Must-do's for the day?

....

....

Mid-Day Check-In

I am grateful for ....

Reflection

Anything about today that I would change?

....

....

Three Amazing things that happened today (big or small)?

1) ....

2) ....

3) ....

Projection

My desires/approach for tomorrow:

....

....

....

Date:____/____/____

Intention:

Today I affirm:..

Three Things That Would Make Today Great:

1) ....

2) ....

3) ....

Must-do's for the day?

\
\
\

Mid-Day Check-In

I am grateful for ....

Reflection

Anything about today that I would change?

\
\
\

Three Amazing things that happened today (big or small)?

1) ....

2) ....

3) ....

Projection

My desires/approach for tomorrow:

\
\

Date: ___/___/___

Intention:

Today I affirm: ....

Three Things That Would Make Today Great:

1) ....

2) ....

3) ....

Must-do's for the day?

....

....

....

Mid-Day Check-In

I am grateful for ....

Reflection

Anything about today that I would change?

....

....

....

Three Amazing things that happened today (big or small)?

1) ....

2) ....

3) ....

Projection

My desires/approach for tomorrow:

....

....

Date: ___/___/___

Intention:

Today I affirm:..

Three Things That Would Make Today Great:

1) ....

2) ....

3) ....

Must-do's for the day?

....

....

....

Mid-Day Check-In

I am grateful for ....

Reflection

Anything about today that I would change?

....

....

....

Three Amazing things that happened today (big or small)?

1) ....

2) ....

3) ....

Projection

My desires/approach for tomorrow:

....

....

....

Date: ___ / ___ / ___

Intention:

Today I affirm: ....

Three Things That Would Make Today Great:

1) ....

2) ....

3) ....

Must-do's for the day?

....

....

....

Mid-Day Check-In

I am grateful for ....

Reflection

Anything about today that I would change?

....

....

....

Three Amazing things that happened today (big or small)?

1) ....

2) ....

3) ....

Projection

My desires/approach for tomorrow:

....

....

....

Date: ___/___/___

Intention:

Today I affirm:...

Three Things That Would Make Today Great:

1) ....

2) ....

3) ....

Must-do's for the day?

....

....

Mid-Day Check-In

I am grateful for ....

Reflection

Anything about today that I would change?

....

....

....

Three Amazing things that happened today (big or small)?

1) ....

2) ....

3) ....

Projection

My desires/approach for tomorrow:

....

....

....

Date:___/___/___

Intention:

Today I affirm:..

Three Things That Would Make Today Great:

1) ....

2) ....

3) ....

Must-do's for the day?

....

....

Mid-Day Check-In

I am grateful for ....

Reflection

Anything about today that I would change?

....

....

....

Three Amazing things that happened today (big or small)?

1) ....

2) ....

3) ....

Projection

My desires/approach for tomorrow:

....

....

Date: ___ / ___ / ___

Intention:

Today I affirm: ....

Three Things That Would Make Today Great:

1) ....

2) ....

3) ....

Must-do's for the day?

....

....

Mid-Day Check-In

I am grateful for ....

Reflection

Anything about today that I would change?

....

....

Three Amazing things that happened today (big or small)?

1) ....

2) ....

3) ....

Projection

My desires/approach for tomorrow:

....

....

Date: ___ / ___ / ___

Intention:

Today I affirm: ....

Three Things That Would Make Today Great:

1) ....

2) ....

3) ....

Must-do's for the day?

....

....

Mid-Day Check-In

I am grateful for ....

Reflection

Anything about today that I would change?

....

....

Three Amazing things that happened today (big or small)?

1) ....

2) ....

3) ....

Projection

My desires/approach for tomorrow:

....

....

Date: ___ / ___ / ___

Intention:

Today I affirm: _____

Three Things That Would Make Today Great:

1) _____

2) _____

3) _____

Must-do's for the day?

_____

_____

Mid-Day Check-In

I am grateful for _____

Reflection

Anything about today that I would change?

_____

_____

_____

Three Amazing things that happened today (big or small)?

1) _____

2) _____

3) _____

Projection

My desires/approach for tomorrow:

_____

_____

_____

Date: ___ / ___ / ___

Intention:

Today I affirm: ....

Three Things That Would Make Today Great:

1) ....

2) ....

3) ....

Must-do's for the day?

....

....

....

Mid-Day Check-In

I am grateful for ....

Reflection

Anything about today that I would change?

....

....

....

Three Amazing things that happened today (big or small)?

1) ....

2) ....

3) ....

Projection

My desires/approach for tomorrow:

....

....

....

Date:_____/_____/_____

Intention:

Today I affirm:_____

Three Things That Would Make Today Great:

1) ....

2) ....

3) ....

Must-do's for the day?

....

....

....

Mid-Day Check-In

I am grateful for ....

Reflection

Anything about today that I would change?

....

....

....

Three Amazing things that happened today (big or small)?

1) ....

2) ....

3) ....

Projection

My desires/approach for tomorrow:

....

....

....

Date: ____/____/____

Intention:

Today I affirm: ....

Three Things That Would Make Today Great:

1) ....

2) ....

3) ....

Must-do's for the day?

....

....

....

Mid-Day Check-In

I am grateful for ....

Reflection

Anything about today that I would change?

....

....

....

Three Amazing things that happened today (big or small)?

1) ....

2) ....

3) ....

Projection

My desires/approach for tomorrow:

....

....

....

Date: ____ / ____ / ____

Intention:

Today I affirm:..

Three Things That Would Make Today Great:

1) ....

2) ....

3) ....

Must-do's for the day?

....

....

Mid-Day Check-In

I am grateful for ....

Reflection

Anything about today that I would change?

....

....

Three Amazing things that happened today (big or small)?

1) ....

2) ....

3) ....

Projection

My desires/approach for tomorrow:

....

....

Date: ___/___/___

Intention:

Today I affirm:..

Three Things That Would Make Today Great:

1) ....

2) ....

3) ....

Must-do's for the day?

....

....

Mid-Day Check-In

I am grateful for ....

Reflection

Anything about today that I would change?

....

....

....

Three Amazing things that happened today (big or small)?

1) ....

2) ....

3) ....

Projection

My desires/approach for tomorrow:

....

....

....

Date:_____/_____/_____

Intention:

Today I affirm:..

Three Things That Would Make Today Great:

1) ....

2) ....

3) ....

Must-do's for the day?

....

....

Mid-Day Check-In

I am grateful for ....

Reflection

Anything about today that I would change?

....

....

....

Three Amazing things that happened today (big or small)?

1) ....

2) ....

3) ....

Projection

My desires/approach for tomorrow:

....

....

....

Date: ___ / ___ / ___

Intention:

Today I affirm:...

Three Things That Would Make Today Great:

1) ....

2) ....

3) ....

Must-do's for the day?

....

....

Mid-Day Check-In

I am grateful for ....

Reflection

Anything about today that I would change?

....

....

Three Amazing things that happened today (big or small)?

1) ....

2) ....

3) ....

Projection

My desires/approach for tomorrow:

....

....

....

Date: ___ / ___ / ___

Intention:

Today I affirm:_____

Three Things That Would Make Today Great:

1) _____

2) _____

3) _____

Must-do's for the day?

_____

_____

Mid-Day Check-In

I am grateful for _____

Reflection

Anything about today that I would change?

_____

_____

Three Amazing things that happened today (big or small)?

1) _____

2) _____

3) _____

Projection

My desires/approach for tomorrow:

_____

_____

Date: ___ / ___ / ___

Intention:

Today I affirm:...

Three Things That Would Make Today Great:

1) ....

2) ....

3) ....

Must-do's for the day?

....

....

Mid-Day Check-In

I am grateful for ....

Reflection

Anything about today that I would change?

....

....

Three Amazing things that happened today (big or small)?

1) ....

2) ....

3) ....

Projection

My desires/approach for tomorrow:

....

....

....

Date:_____/_____/_____

Intention:

Today I affirm:...

Three Things That Would Make Today Great:

1) ....

2) ....

3) ....

Must-do's for the day?

....

....

Mid-Day Check-In

I am grateful for ....

Reflection

Anything about today that I would change?

....

....

Three Amazing things that happened today (big or small)?

1) ....

2) ....

3) ....

Projection

My desires/approach for tomorrow:

....

....

Date: ____/____/____

Intention:

Today I affirm: ....

Three Things That Would Make Today Great:

1) ....

2) ....

3) ....

Must-do's for the day?

....

....

Mid-Day Check-In

I am grateful for ....

Reflection

Anything about today that I would change?

....

....

....

Three Amazing things that happened today (big or small)?

1) ....

2) ....

3) ....

Projection

My desires/approach for tomorrow:

....

....

Date: ___ / ___ / ___

Intention:

Today I affirm:...

Three Things That Would Make Today Great:

1) ....

2) ....

3) ....

Must-do's for the day?

....

....

....

Mid-Day Check-In

I am grateful for ....

Reflection

Anything about today that I would change?

....

....

....

Three Amazing things that happened today (big or small)?

1) ....

2) ....

3) ....

Projection

My desires/approach for tomorrow:

....

....

....

Date: ___/___/___

Intention:

Today I affirm: ....

Three Things That Would Make Today Great:

1) ....

2) ....

3) ....

Must-do's for the day?

....

....

....

Mid-Day Check-In

I am grateful for ....

Reflection

Anything about today that I would change?

....

....

....

Three Amazing things that happened today (big or small)?

1) ....

2) ....

3) ....

Projection

My desires/approach for tomorrow:

....

....

....

Date: ___/___/___

Intention:

Today I affirm:...

Three Things That Would Make Today Great:

1) ....

2) ....

3) ....

Must-do's for the day?

....

....

Mid-Day Check-In

I am grateful for ....

Reflection

Anything about today that I would change?

....

....

....

Three Amazing things that happened today (big or small)?

1) ....

2) ....

3) ....

Projection

My desires/approach for tomorrow:

....

....

Date:____/____/____

Intention:

Today I affirm:..

Three Things That Would Make Today Great:

1) ....

2) ....

3) ....

Must-do's for the day?

....

....

....

Mid-Day Check-In

I am grateful for ....

Reflection

Anything about today that I would change?

....

....

....

Three Amazing things that happened today (big or small)?

1) ....

2) ....

3) ....

Projection

My desires/approach for tomorrow:

....

....

....

Date: ___/___/___

Intention:

Today I affirm: _____

Three Things That Would Make Today Great:

1) _____

2) _____

3) _____

Must-do's for the day?

_____

_____

Mid-Day Check-In

I am grateful for _____

Reflection

Anything about today that I would change?

_____

_____

_____

Three Amazing things that happened today (big or small)?

1) _____

2) _____

3) _____

Projection

My desires/approach for tomorrow:

_____

_____

Date:___/___/___

Intention:

Today I affirm:..

Three Things That Would Make Today Great:

1) ....

2) ....

3) ....

Must-do's for the day?

....

....

....

Mid-Day Check-In

I am grateful for ....

Reflection

Anything about today that I would change?

....

....

....

....

Three Amazing things that happened today (big or small)?

1) ....

2) ....

3) ....

Projection

My desires/approach for tomorrow:

....

....

....

Date:_____ / _____ / _____

Intention:

Today I affirm:...

Three Things That Would Make Today Great:

1) ....

2) ....

3) ....

Must-do's for the day?

....

....

Mid-Day Check-In

I am grateful for ....

Reflection

Anything about today that I would change?

....

....

....

Three Amazing things that happened today (big or small)?

1) ....

2) ....

3) ....

Projection

My desires/approach for tomorrow:

....

....

Date: _____ / _____ / _____

Intention:

Today I affirm:...

Three Things That Would Make Today Great:

1) ....

2) ....

3) ....

Must-do's for the day?

....

....

....

Mid-Day Check-In

I am grateful for ....

Reflection

Anything about today that I would change?

....

....

....

Three Amazing things that happened today (big or small)?

1) ....

2) ....

3) ....

Projection

My desires/approach for tomorrow:

....

....

....

Date:___/___/___

Intention:

Today I affirm:_____

Three Things That Would Make Today Great:

1) _____

2) _____

3) _____

Must-do's for the day?

_____

_____

Mid-Day Check-In

I am grateful for _____

Reflection

Anything about today that I would change?

_____

_____

_____

Three Amazing things that happened today (big or small)?

1) _____

2) _____

3) _____

Projection

My desires/approach for tomorrow:

_____

_____

Date: ___/___/___

Intention:

Today I affirm: ....

Three Things That Would Make Today Great:

1) ....

2) ....

3) ....

Must-do's for the day?

....

....

Mid-Day Check-In

I am grateful for ....

Reflection

Anything about today that I would change?

....

....

....

Three Amazing things that happened today (big or small)?

1) ....

2) ....

3) ....

Projection

My desires/approach for tomorrow:

....

....

Date: ___/___/___

Intention:

Today I affirm:...

Three Things That Would Make Today Great:

1) ....

2) ....

3) ....

Must-do's for the day?

....

....

Mid-Day Check-In

I am grateful for ....

Reflection

Anything about today that I would change?

....

....

....

Three Amazing things that happened today (big or small)?

1) ....

2) ....

3) ....

Projection

My desires/approach for tomorrow:

....

....

Date: ____/____/____

Intention:

Today I affirm:...

Three Things That Would Make Today Great:

1) ....

2) ....

3) ....

Must-do's for the day?

....

....

....

Mid-Day Check-In

I am grateful for ....

Reflection

Anything about today that I would change?

....

....

....

Three Amazing things that happened today (big or small)?

1) ....

2) ....

3) ....

Projection

My desires/approach for tomorrow:

....

....

....

Date: ___/___/___

Intention:

Today I affirm: _____

Three Things That Would Make Today Great:

1) ....

2) ....

3) ....

Must-do's for the day?

....

....

Mid-Day Check-In

I am grateful for ....

Reflection

Anything about today that I would change?

....

....

....

Three Amazing things that happened today (big or small)?

1) ....

2) ....

3) ....

Projection

My desires/approach for tomorrow:

....

....

Date:_____/_____/_____

Intention:

Today I affirm:...

Three Things That Would Make Today Great:

1) ....

2) ....

3) ....

Must-do's for the day?

....

....

Mid-Day Check-In

I am grateful for ....

Reflection

Anything about today that I would change?

....

....

....

Three Amazing things that happened today (big or small)?

1) ....

2) ....

3) ....

Projection

My desires/approach for tomorrow:

....

....

....

Date:_____/_____/_____

Intention:

Today I affirm:...

Three Things That Would Make Today Great:

1) ....

2) ....

3) ....

Must-do's for the day?

....

....

Mid-Day Check-In

I am grateful for...

Reflection

Anything about today that I would change?

....

....

....

Three Amazing things that happened today (big or small)?

1) ....

2) ....

3) ....

Projection

My desires/approach for tomorrow:

....

....

Date: ___ / ___ / ___

Intention:

Today I affirm: ....

Three Things That Would Make Today Great:

1) ....

2) ....

3) ....

Must-do's for the day?

....

....

....

Mid-Day Check-In

I am grateful for ....

Reflection

Anything about today that I would change?

....

....

....

Three Amazing things that happened today (big or small)?

1) ....

2) ....

3) ....

Projection

My desires/approach for tomorrow:

....

....

....

Date: ___/___/___

Intention:

Today I affirm:...

Three Things That Would Make Today Great:

1) ....

2) ....

3) ....

Must-do's for the day?

....

....

....

Mid-Day Check-In

I am grateful for ....

Reflection

Anything about today that I would change?

....

....

....

Three Amazing things that happened today (big or small)?

1) ....

2) ....

3) ....

Projection

My desires/approach for tomorrow:

....

....

....

Date: ___/___/___

Intention:

Today I affirm: ....

Three Things That Would Make Today Great:

1) ....

2) ....

3) ....

Must-do's for the day?

....

....

Mid-Day Check-In

I am grateful for ....

Reflection

Anything about today that I would change?

....

....

Three Amazing things that happened today (big or small)?

1) ....

2) ....

3) ....

Projection

My desires/approach for tomorrow:

....

....

....

Date: ___ / ___ / ___

Intention:

Today I affirm:_____

Three Things That Would Make Today Great:

1) _____

2) _____

3) _____

Must-do's for the day?

_____

_____

_____

Mid-Day Check-In

I am grateful for _____

Reflection

Anything about today that I would change?

_____

_____

_____

Three Amazing things that happened today (big or small)?

1) _____

2) _____

3) _____

Projection

My desires/approach for tomorrow:

_____

_____

_____

Date:___/___/___

Intention:

Today I affirm:...

Three Things That Would Make Today Great:

1) ....

2) ....

3) ....

Must-do's for the day?

....

....

Mid-Day Check-In

I am grateful for...

Reflection

Anything about today that I would change?

....

....

....

Three Amazing things that happened today (big or small)?

1) ....

2) ....

3) ....

Projection

My desires/approach for tomorrow:

....

....

Date:_____/_____/_____

Intention:

Today I affirm:_____

Three Things That Would Make Today Great:

1) ....

2) ....

3) ....

Must-do's for the day?

....

....

Mid-Day Check-In

I am grateful for ....

Reflection

Anything about today that I would change?

....

....

....

Three Amazing things that happened today (big or small)?

1) ....

2) ....

3) ....

Projection

My desires/approach for tomorrow:

....

....

....

Date: _____ / _____ / _____

Intention:

Today I affirm:...

Three Things That Would Make Today Great:

1) ....

2) ....

3) ....

Must-do's for the day?

....

....

Mid-Day Check-In

I am grateful for ....

Reflection

Anything about today that I would change?

....

....

Three Amazing things that happened today (big or small)?

1) ....

2) ....

3) ....

Projection

My desires/approach for tomorrow:

....

....

Date:____/____/____

Intention:

Today I affirm:...

Three Things That Would Make Today Great:

1) ....

2) ....

3) ....

Must-do's for the day?

....

....

Mid-Day Check-In

I am grateful for ....

Reflection

Anything about today that I would change?

....

....

Three Amazing things that happened today (big or small)?

1) ....

2) ....

3) ....

Projection

My desires/approach for tomorrow:

....

....

Date:___/___/___

Intention:

Today I affirm:...

Three Things That Would Make Today Great:

1) ....

2) ....

3) ....

Must-do's for the day?

....

....

Mid-Day Check-In

I am grateful for ....

Reflection

Anything about today that I would change?

....

....

Three Amazing things that happened today (big or small)?

1) ....

2) ....

3) ....

Projection

My desires/approach for tomorrow:

....

....

Date: ___/___/___

Intention:

Today I affirm:...

Three Things That Would Make Today Great:

1) ....

2) ....

3) ....

Must-do's for the day?

....

....

Mid-Day Check-In

I am grateful for ....

Reflection

Anything about today that I would change?

....

....

....

Three Amazing things that happened today (big or small)?

1) ....

2) ....

3) ....

Projection

My desires/approach for tomorrow:

....

....

....

Date: ___/___/___

Intention:

Today I affirm:..

Three Things That Would Make Today Great:

1) ....

2) ....

3) ....

Must-do's for the day?

....

....

....

Mid-Day Check-In

I am grateful for ....

Reflection

Anything about today that I would change?

....

....

....

Three Amazing things that happened today (big or small)?

1) ....

2) ....

3) ....

Projection

My desires/approach for tomorrow:

....

....

....

Date: ___/___/___

Intention:

Today I affirm: ....

1) ....

2) ....

3) ....

Must-do's for the day?

....

....

Mid-Day Check-In

I am grateful for ....

Reflection

Anything about today that I would change?

....

....

Three Amazing things that happened today (big or small)?

1) ....

2) ....

3) ....

Projection

My desires/approach for tomorrow:

....

....

Date: ___/___/___

Intention:

Today I affirm:...

Three Things That Would Make Today Great:

1) ....

2) ....

3) ....

Must-do's for the day?

....

....

Mid-Day Check-In

I am grateful for ....

Reflection

Anything about today that I would change?

....

....

Three Amazing things that happened today (big or small)?

1) ....

2) ....

3) ....

Projection

My desires/approach for tomorrow:

....

....

Date: ___/___/___

Intention:

Today I affirm: ....

Three Things That Would Make Today Great:

1) ....

2) ....

3) ....

Must-do's for the day?

....

....

Mid-Day Check-In

I am grateful for ....

Reflection

Anything about today that I would change?

....

....

....

Three Amazing things that happened today (big or small)?

1) ....

2) ....

3) ....

Projection

My desires/approach for tomorrow:

....

....

Date: ___ / ___ / ___

Intention:

Today I affirm:...

Three Things That Would Make Today Great:

1) ....

2) ....

3) ....

Must-do's for the day?

....

....

Mid-Day Check-In

I am grateful for ....

Reflection

Anything about today that I would change?

....

....

Three Amazing things that happened today (big or small)?

1) ....

2) ....

3) ....

Projection

My desires/approach for tomorrow:

....

....

....

Date:_____/_____/_____

Intention:

Today I affirm:_____

Three Things That Would Make Today Great:

1) ....

2) ....

3) ....

Must-do's for the day?

....

....

Mid-Day Check-In

I am grateful for _____

Reflection

Anything about today that I would change?

....

....

....

Three Amazing things that happened today (big or small)?

1) ....

2) ....

3) ....

Projection

My desires/approach for tomorrow:

....

....

....

Date:___/___/___

Intention:

Today I affirm:..

Three Things That Would Make Today Great:

1) ....

2) ....

3) ....

Must-do's for the day?

....

....

Mid-Day Check-In

I am grateful for ....

Reflection

Anything about today that I would change?

....

....

Three Amazing things that happened today (big or small)?

1) ....

2) ....

3) ....

Projection

My desires/approach for tomorrow:

....

....

Date:_____/_____/_____

Intention:

Today I affirm:...

Three Things That Would Make Today Great:

1) ....

2) ....

3) ....

Must-do's for the day?

....

....

Mid-Day Check-In

I am grateful for ....

Reflection

Anything about today that I would change?

....

....

....

Three Amazing things that happened today (big or small)?

1) ....

2) ....

3) ....

Projection

My desires/approach for tomorrow:

....

....

....

Date: ___/___/___

Intention:

Today I affirm:...

Three Things That Would Make Today Great:

1) ....

2) ....

3) ....

Must-do's for the day?

....

....

Mid-Day Check-In

I am grateful for ....

Reflection

Anything about today that I would change?

....

....

....

Three Amazing things that happened today (big or small)?

1) ....

2) ....

3) ....

Projection

My desires/approach for tomorrow:

....

....

Date: ___/___/___

Intention:

Today I affirm: ....

Three Things That Would Make Today Great:

1) ....

2) ....

3) ....

Must-do's for the day?

....

....

....

Mid-Day Check-In

I am grateful for ....

Reflection

Anything about today that I would change?

....

....

....

Three Amazing things that happened today (big or small)?

1) ....

2) ....

3) ....

Projection

My desires/approach for tomorrow:

....

....

....

Date: ___/___/___

Intention:

Today I affirm:...

Three Things That Would Make Today Great:

1) ....

2) ....

3) ....

Must-do's for the day?

....

....

....

Mid-Day Check-In

I am grateful for ....

Reflection

Anything about today that I would change?

....

....

....

Three Amazing things that happened today (big or small)?

1) ....

2) ....

3) ....

Projection

My desires/approach for tomorrow:

....

....

....

Date: ___ / ___ / ___

Intention:

Today I affirm: ....

Three Things That Would Make Today Great:

1) ....

2) ....

3) ....

Must-do's for the day?

....

....

Mid-Day Check-In

I am grateful for ....

Reflection

Anything about today that I would change?

....

....

Three Amazing things that happened today (big or small)?

1) ....

2) ....

3) ....

Projection

My desires/approach for tomorrow:

....

....

....

Date: ___ / ___ / ___

Intention:

Today I affirm: ....

Three Things That Would Make Today Great:

1) ....

2) ....

3) ....

Must-do's for the day?

....

....

Mid-Day Check-In

I am grateful for ....

Reflection

Anything about today that I would change?

....

....

....

Three Amazing things that happened today (big or small)?

1) ....

2) ....

3) ....

Projection

My desires/approach for tomorrow:

....

....

Date:_____/_____/_____

Intention:

Today I affirm:..

Three Things That Would Make Today Great:

1) ....

2) ....

3) ....

Must-do's for the day?

....

....

Mid-Day Check-In

I am grateful for ....

Reflection

Anything about today that I would change?

....

....

....

Three Amazing things that happened today (big or small)?

1) ....

2) ....

3) ....

Projection

My desires/approach for tomorrow:

....

....

Date: ___/___/___

Intention:

Today I affirm:...

Three Things That Would Make Today Great:

1) ....

2) ....

3) ....

Must-do's for the day?

....

....

Mid-Day Check-In

I am grateful for ....

Reflection

Anything about today that I would change?

....

....

Three Amazing things that happened today (big or small)?

1) ....

2) ....

3) ....

Projection

My desires/approach for tomorrow:

....

....

Date: ___ / ___ / ___

Intention:

Today I affirm: ....

Three Things That Would Make Today Great:

1) ....

2) ....

3) ....

Must-do's for the day?

....

....

Mid-Day Check-In

I am grateful for ....

Reflection

Anything about today that I would change?

....

....

....

Three Amazing things that happened today (big or small)?

1) ....

2) ....

3) ....

Projection

My desires/approach for tomorrow:

....

....

....

Date: ___/___/___

Intention:

Today I affirm:..

Three Things That Would Make Today Great:

1) ....

2) ....

3) ....

Must-do's for the day?

....

....

....

Mid-Day Check-In

I am grateful for ....

Reflection

Anything about today that I would change?

....

....

....

Three Amazing things that happened today (big or small)?

1) ....

2) ....

3) ....

Projection

My desires/approach for tomorrow:

....

....

....

Date: _____ / _____ / _____

Intention:

Today I affirm: ....

Three Things That Would Make Today Great:

1) ....

2) ....

3) ....

Must-do's for the day?

....

....

Mid-Day Check-In

I am grateful for ....

Reflection

Anything about today that I would change?

....

....

Three Amazing things that happened today (big or small)?

1) ....

2) ....

3) ....

Projection

My desires/approach for tomorrow:

....

....

Date: ___ / ___ / ___

Intention:

Today I affirm: ....

1) ....

2) ....

3) ....

Must-do's for the day?

....

....

....

Mid-Day Check-In

I am grateful for ....

Reflection

Anything about today that I would change?

....

....

....

Three Amazing things that happened today (big or small)?

1) ....

2) ....

3) ....

Projection

My desires/approach for tomorrow:

....

....

....

Date: ____/____/____

Intention:

Today I affirm:...

Three Things That Would Make Today Great:

1) ....

2) ....

3) ....

Must-do's for the day?

....

....

....

Mid-Day Check-In

I am grateful for ....

Reflection

Anything about today that I would change?

....

....

....

Three Amazing things that happened today (big or small)?

1) ....

2) ....

3) ....

Projection

My desires/approach for tomorrow:

....

....

....

Date:_____/_____/_____

Intention:

Today I affirm:...

Three Things That Would Make Today Great:

1) ....

2) ....

3) ....

Must-do's for the day?

....

....

Mid-Day Check-In

I am grateful for ....

Reflection

Anything about today that I would change?

....

....

....

Three Amazing things that happened today (big or small)?

1) ....

2) ....

3) ....

Projection

My desires/approach for tomorrow:

....

....

Date:____/____/____

Intention:

Today I affirm:...

Three Things That Would Make Today Great:

1) ....

2) ....

3) ....

Must-do's for the day?

....

....

....

Mid-Day Check-In

I am grateful for ....

Reflection

Anything about today that I would change?

....

....

....

Three Amazing things that happened today (big or small)?

1) ....

2) ....

3) ....

Projection

My desires/approach for tomorrow:

....

....

Date:____/____/____

Intention:

Today I affirm:..

Three Things That Would Make Today Great:

1) ....

2) ....

3) ....

Must-do's for the day?

....

....

Mid-Day Check-In

I am grateful for ....

Reflection

Anything about today that I would change?

....

....

....

Three Amazing things that happened today (big or small)?

1) ....

2) ....

3) ....

Projection

My desires/approach for tomorrow:

....

....

Date: ___ / ___ / ___

Intention:

Today I affirm:_____

Three Things That Would Make Today Great:

1) ....

2) ....

3) ....

Must-do's for the day?

....

....

....

Mid-Day Check-In

I am grateful for _____

Reflection

Anything about today that I would change?

....

....

....

Three Amazing things that happened today (big or small)?

1) ....

2) ....

3) ....

Projection

My desires/approach for tomorrow:

....

....

....

Date:_____/_____/_____

Intention:

Today I affirm:..

Three Things That Would Make Today Great:

1) ....

2) ....

3) ....

Must-do's for the day?

....

....

Mid-Day Check-In

I am grateful for ....

Reflection

Anything about today that I would change?

....

....

Three Amazing things that happened today (big or small)?

1) ....

2) ....

3) ....

Projection

My desires/approach for tomorrow:

....

....

Date: ___/___/___

Intention:

Today I affirm:...

Three Things That Would Make Today Great:

1) ....

2) ....

3) ....

Must-do's for the day?

....

....

Mid-Day Check-In

I am grateful for ....

Reflection

Anything about today that I would change?

....

....

Three Amazing things that happened today (big or small)?

1) ....

2) ....

3) ....

Projection

My desires/approach for tomorrow:

....

....

....

Date:_____/_____/_____

Intention:

Today I affirm:..

Three Things That Would Make Today Great:

1) ....

2) ....

3) ....

Must-do's for the day?

....

....

Mid-Day Check-In

I am grateful for ....

Reflection

Anything about today that I would change?

....

....

....

Three Amazing things that happened today (big or small)?

1) ....

2) ....

3) ....

Projection

My desires/approach for tomorrow:

....

....

....

Date:____/____/____

Intention:

Today I affirm:..

Three Things That Would Make Today Great:

1) ....

2) ....

3) ....

Must-do's for the day?

....

....

Mid-Day Check-In

I am grateful for ....

Reflection

Anything about today that I would change?

....

....

....

Three Amazing things that happened today (big or small)?

1) ....

2) ....

3) ....

Projection

My desires/approach for tomorrow:

....

....

Date:_____/_____/_____

Intention:

Today I affirm:...

Three Things That Would Make Today Great:

1) ....

2) ....

3) ....

Must-do's for the day?

....

....

Mid-Day Check-In

I am grateful for ....

Reflection

Anything about today that I would change?

....

....

....

Three Amazing things that happened today (big or small)?

1) ....

2) ....

3) ....

Projection

My desires/approach for tomorrow:

....

....

Date:_____/_____/_____

Intention:

Today I affirm:...

Three Things That Would Make Today Great:

1) ....

2) ....

3) ....

Must-do's for the day?

....

....

Mid-Day Check-In

I am grateful for ....

Reflection

Anything about today that I would change?

....

....

....

Three Amazing things that happened today (big or small)?

1) ....

2) ....

3) ....

Projection

My desires/approach for tomorrow:

....

....

Date: ___ / ___ / ___

Intention:

Today I affirm:...

Three Things That Would Make Today Great:

1) ....

2) ....

3) ....

Must-do's for the day?

....

....

Mid-Day Check-In

I am grateful for ....

Reflection

Anything about today that I would change?

....

....

....

Three Amazing things that happened today (big or small)?

1) ....

2) ....

3) ....

Projection

My desires/approach for tomorrow:

....

....

....

Date: ___/___/___

Intention:

Today I affirm:...

Three Things That Would Make Today Great:

1) ....

2) ....

3) ....

Must-do's for the day?

....

....

Mid-Day Check-In

I am grateful for ....

Reflection

Anything about today that I would change?

....

....

Three Amazing things that happened today (big or small)?

1) ....

2) ....

3) ....

Projection

My desires/approach for tomorrow:

....

....

Date: ___ / ___ / ___

Intention:

Today I affirm: ....

Three Things That Would Make Today Great:

1) ....

2) ....

3) ....

Must-do's for the day?

....

....

Mid-Day Check-In

I am grateful for ....

Reflection

Anything about today that I would change?

....

....

....

Three Amazing things that happened today (big or small)?

1) ....

2) ....

3) ....

Projection

My desires/approach for tomorrow:

....

....

Date: ___ / ___ / ___

Intention:

Today I affirm: ....

Three Things That Would Make Today Great:

1) ....

2) ....

3) ....

Must-do's for the day?

....

....

Mid-Day Check-In

I am grateful for ....

Reflection

Anything about today that I would change?

....

....

....

Three Amazing things that happened today (big or small)?

1) ....

2) ....

3) ....

Projection

My desires/approach for tomorrow:

....

....

Date: ___/___/___

Intention:

Today I affirm:...

Three Things That Would Make Today Great:

1) ....

2) ....

3) ....

Must-do's for the day?

....

....

Mid-Day Check-In

I am grateful for ....

Reflection

Anything about today that I would change?

....

....

....

Three Amazing things that happened today (big or small)?

1) ....

2) ....

3) ....

Projection

My desires/approach for tomorrow:

....

....

Date:_____/_____/_____

Intention:

Today I affirm:..

Three Things That Would Make Today Great:

1) ....

2) ....

3) ....

Must-do's for the day?

....

....

Mid-Day Check-In

I am grateful for ....

Reflection

Anything about today that I would change?

....

....

....

Three Amazing things that happened today (big or small)?

1) ....

2) ....

3) ....

Projection

My desires/approach for tomorrow:

....

....

Date: ___/___/___

Intention:

Today I affirm: ....

Three Things That Would Make Today Great:

1) ....

2) ....

3) ....

Must-do's for the day?

....

....

Mid-Day Check-In

I am grateful for ....

Reflection

Anything about today that I would change?

....

....

....

Three Amazing things that happened today (big or small)?

1) ....

2) ....

3) ....

Projection

My desires/approach for tomorrow:

....

....

....

Date: ___/___/___

Intention:

Today I affirm:...

Three Things That Would Make Today Great:

1) ....

2) ....

3) ....

Must-do's for the day?

Mid-Day Check-In

I am grateful for ....

Reflection

Anything about today that I would change?

Three Amazing things that happened today (big or small)?

1) ....

2) ....

3) ....

Projection

My desires/approach for tomorrow:

Date:___/___/___

Intention:

Today I affirm:...

Three Things That Would Make Today Great:

1) ....

2) ....

3) ....

Must-do's for the day?

....

....

Mid-Day Check-In

I am grateful for ....

Reflection

Anything about today that I would change?

....

....

....

Three Amazing things that happened today (big or small)?

1) ....

2) ....

3) ....

Projection

My desires/approach for tomorrow:

....

....

Date: ___ / ___ / ___

Intention:

Today I affirm:

Three Things That Would Make Today Great:

1)

2)

3)

Must-do's for the day?

Mid-Day Check-In

I am grateful for

Reflection

Anything about today that I would change?

Three Amazing things that happened today (big or small)?

1)

2)

3)

Projection

My desires/approach for tomorrow:

Date:___/___/___

Intention:

Today I affirm:...

Three Things That Would Make Today Great:

1) ....

2) ....

3) ....

Must-do's for the day?

....

....

Mid-Day Check-In

I am grateful for ....

Reflection

Anything about today that I would change?

....

....

....

Three Amazing things that happened today (big or small)?

1) ....

2) ....

3) ....

Projection

My desires/approach for tomorrow:

....

....

....

Date: ___ / ___ / ___

Intention:

Today I affirm:..

Three Things That Would Make Today Great:

1) ....

2) ....

3) ....

Must-do's for the day?

....

....

Mid-Day Check-In

I am grateful for ....

Reflection

Anything about today that I would change?

....

....

....

Three Amazing things that happened today (big or small)?

1) ....

2) ....

3) ....

Projection

My desires/approach for tomorrow:

....

....

....

Date: ___/___/___

Intention:

Today I affirm:..

Three Things That Would Make Today Great:

1) ....

2) ....

3) ....

Must-do's for the day?

....

....

Mid-Day Check-In

I am grateful for ....

Reflection

Anything about today that I would change?

....

....

....

Three Amazing things that happened today (big or small)?

1) ....

2) ....

3) ....

Projection

My desires/approach for tomorrow:

....

....

....

Date: ___/___/___

Intention:

Today I affirm: ....

Three Things That Would Make Today Great:

1) ....

2) ....

3) ....

Must-do's for the day?

....

....

....

Mid-Day Check-In

I am grateful for ....

Reflection

Anything about today that I would change?

....

....

....

Three Amazing things that happened today (big or small)?

1) ....

2) ....

3) ....

Projection

My desires/approach for tomorrow:

....

....

....

Date: ___/___/___

Intention:

Today I affirm:..

Three Things That Would Make Today Great:

1) ....

2) ....

3) ....

Must-do's for the day?

....

....

Mid-Day Check-In

I am grateful for ....

Reflection

Anything about today that I would change?

....

....

Three Amazing things that happened today (big or small)?

1) ....

2) ....

3) ....

Projection

My desires/approach for tomorrow:

....

....

Date: ___/___/___

Intention:

Today I affirm:..

Three Things That Would Make Today Great:

1) ....

2) ....

3) ....

Must-do's for the day?

....

....

....

Mid-Day Check-In

I am grateful for ....

Reflection

Anything about today that I would change?

....

....

....

Three Amazing things that happened today (big or small)?

1) ....

2) ....

3) ....

Projection

My desires/approach for tomorrow:

....

....

....

Date:____/____/____

Intention:

Today I affirm:...

Three Things That Would Make Today Great:

1) ....

2) ....

3) ....

Must-do's for the day?

....

....

Mid-Day Check-In

I am grateful for ....

Reflection

Anything about today that I would change?

....

....

....

Three Amazing things that happened today (big or small)?

1) ....

2) ....

3) ....

Projection

My desires/approach for tomorrow:

....

....

....

Date: _____/_____/_____

Intention:

Today I affirm:..

Three Things That Would Make Today Great:

1) ....

2) ....

3) ....

Must-do's for the day?

....

....

....

Mid-Day Check-In

I am grateful for ....

Reflection

Anything about today that I would change?

....

....

....

Three Amazing things that happened today (big or small)?

1) ....

2) ....

3) ....

Projection

My desires/approach for tomorrow:

....

....

Date:_____/_____/_____

Intention:

Today I affirm:...

Three Things That Would Make Today Great:

1) ....

2) ....

3) ....

Must-do's for the day?

....

....

Mid-Day Check-In

I am grateful for ....

Reflection

Anything about today that I would change?

....

....

....

Three Amazing things that happened today (big or small)?

1) ....

2) ....

3) ....

Projection

My desires/approach for tomorrow:

....

....

Date: ____ / ____ / ____

Intention:

Today I affirm: ....

Three Things That Would Make Today Great:

1) ....

2) ....

3) ....

Must-do's for the day?

....

....

Mid-Day Check-In

I am grateful for ....

Reflection

Anything about today that I would change?

....

....

Three Amazing things that happened today (big or small)?

1) ....

2) ....

3) ....

Projection

My desires/approach for tomorrow:

....

....

Date: ___/___/___

Intention:

Today I affirm: ....

Three Things That Would Make Today Great:

1) ....

2) ....

3) ....

Must-do's for the day?

....

....

Mid-Day Check-In

I am grateful for ....

Reflection

Anything about today that I would change?

....

....

....

Three Amazing things that happened today (big or small)?

1) ....

2) ....

3) ....

Projection

My desires/approach for tomorrow:

....

....

....

Date: ___/___/___

Intention:

Today I affirm:..

Three Things That Would Make Today Great:

1) ....

2) ....

3) ....

Must-do's for the day?

....

....

Mid-Day Check-In

I am grateful for ....

Reflection

Anything about today that I would change?

....

....

Three Amazing things that happened today (big or small)?

1) ....

2) ....

3) ....

Projection

My desires/approach for tomorrow:

....

....

Date:___/___/___

Intention:

Today I affirm:..

Three Things That Would Make Today Great:

1) ....

2) ....

3) ....

Must-do's for the day?

....

....

Mid-Day Check-In

I am grateful for ....

Reflection

Anything about today that I would change?

....

....

....

Three Amazing things that happened today (big or small)?

1) ....

2) ....

3) ....

Projection

My desires/approach for tomorrow:

....

....

....

Date: ___/___/___

Intention:

Today I affirm:...

Three Things That Would Make Today Great:

1) ....

2) ....

3) ....

Must-do's for the day?

....

....

....

Mid-Day Check-In

I am grateful for ....

Reflection

Anything about today that I would change?

....

....

....

Three Amazing things that happened today (big or small)?

1) ....

2) ....

3) ....

Projection

My desires/approach for tomorrow:

....

....

Date: ___/___/___

Intention:

Today I affirm:..

Three Things That Would Make Today Great:

1) ....

2) ....

3) ....

Must-do's for the day?

....

....

Mid-Day Check-In

I am grateful for ....

Reflection

Anything about today that I would change?

....

....

....

Three Amazing things that happened today (big or small)?

1) ....

2) ....

3) ....

Projection

My desires/approach for tomorrow:

....

....

....

Date:___/___/___

Intention:

Today I affirm:...

Three Things That Would Make Today Great:

1) ....

2) ....

3) ....

Must-do's for the day?

....

....

Mid-Day Check-In

I am grateful for ....

Reflection

Anything about today that I would change?

....

....

....

Three Amazing things that happened today (big or small)?

1) ....

2) ....

3) ....

Projection

My desires/approach for tomorrow:

....

....

....

Date:_____/_____/_____

Intention:

Today I affirm:...

Three Things That Would Make Today Great:

1) ....

2) ....

3) ....

Must-do's for the day?

....

....

....

Mid-Day Check-In

I am grateful for ....

Reflection

Anything about today that I would change?

....

....

....

Three Amazing things that happened today (big or small)?

1) ....

2) ....

3) ....

Projection

My desires/approach for tomorrow:

....

....

....

Date: ___/___/___

Intention:

Today I affirm: ....

Three Things That Would Make Today Great:

1) ....

2) ....

3) ....

Must-do's for the day?

....

....

Mid-Day Check-In

I am grateful for ....

Reflection

Anything about today that I would change?

....

....

Three Amazing things that happened today (big or small)?

1) ....

2) ....

3) ....

Projection

My desires/approach for tomorrow:

....

....

Date: ___/___/___

Intention:

Today I affirm: ....

Three Things That Would Make Today Great:

1) ....

2) ....

3) ....

Must-do's for the day?

....

....

....

Mid-Day Check-In

I am grateful for ....

Reflection

Anything about today that I would change?

....

....

....

Three Amazing things that happened today (big or small)?

1) ....

2) ....

3) ....

Projection

My desires/approach for tomorrow:

....

....

....

Date: ___/___/___

Intention:

Today I affirm:...

Three Things That Would Make Today Great:

1) ....

2) ....

3) ....

Must-do's for the day?

....

....

Mid-Day Check-In

I am grateful for ....

Reflection

Anything about today that I would change?

....

....

....

Three Amazing things that happened today (big or small)?

1) ....

2) ....

3) ....

Projection

My desires/approach for tomorrow:

....

....

....

Date: ___ / ___ / ___

Intention:

Today I affirm: ....

Three Things That Would Make Today Great:

1) ....

2) ....

3) ....

Must-do's for the day?

....

....

Mid-Day Check-In

I am grateful for ....

Reflection

Anything about today that I would change?

....

....

Three Amazing things that happened today (big or small)?

1) ....

2) ....

3) ....

Projection

My desires/approach for tomorrow:

....

....

....

Date: ___ / ___ / ___

Intention:

Today I affirm: ....

Three Things That Would Make Today Great:

1) ....

2) ....

3) ....

Must-do's for the day?

....

....

Mid-Day Check-In

I am grateful for ....

Reflection

Anything about today that I would change?

....

....

Three Amazing things that happened today (big or small)?

1) ....

2) ....

3) ....

Projection

My desires/approach for tomorrow:

....

....

Date:_____/_____/_____

Intention:

Today I affirm:...

Three Things That Would Make Today Great:

1) ....

2) ....

3) ....

Must-do's for the day?

....

....

Mid-Day Check-In

I am grateful for ....

Reflection

Anything about today that I would change?

....

....

....

Three Amazing things that happened today (big or small)?

1) ....

2) ....

3) ....

Projection

My desires/approach for tomorrow:

....

....

....

Date: ___/___/___

Intention:

Today I affirm:...

1) ....

2) ....

3) ....

Must-do's for the day?

....

....

....

Mid-Day Check-In

I am grateful for ....

Reflection

Anything about today that I would change?

....

....

....

Three Amazing things that happened today (big or small)?

1) ....

2) ....

3) ....

Projection

My desires/approach for tomorrow:

....

....

....

Date: ___/___/___

Intention:

Today I affirm: ....

Three Things That Would Make Today Great:

1) ....

2) ....

3) ....

Must-do's for the day?

....

....

Mid-Day Check-In

I am grateful for ....

Reflection

Anything about today that I would change?

....

....

....

Three Amazing things that happened today (big or small)?

1) ....

2) ....

3) ....

Projection

My desires/approach for tomorrow:

....

....

....

Date: ___/___/___

Intention:

Today I affirm:..

1) ....

2) ....

3) ....

Must-do's for the day?

....

....

Mid-Day Check-In

I am grateful for ....

Reflection

Anything about today that I would change?

....

....

Three Amazing things that happened today (big or small)?

1) ....

2) ....

3) ....

Projection

My desires/approach for tomorrow:

....

....

Date: ___/___/___

Intention:

Today I affirm: ....

Three Things That Would Make Today Great:

1) ....

2) ....

3) ....

Must-do's for the day?

....

....

Mid-Day Check-In

I am grateful for ....

Reflection

Anything about today that I would change?

....

....

....

Three Amazing things that happened today (big or small)?

1) ....

2) ....

3) ....

Projection

My desires/approach for tomorrow:

....

....

....

Date: ___/___/___

Intention:

Today I affirm:..

Three Things That Would Make Today Great:

1) ....

2) ....

3) ....

Must-do's for the day?

....

....

Mid-Day Check-In

I am grateful for ....

Reflection

Anything about today that I would change?

....

....

Three Amazing things that happened today (big or small)?

1) ....

2) ....

3) ....

Projection

My desires/approach for tomorrow:

....

....

Date:_____/_____/_____

Intention:

Today I affirm:..

Three Things That Would Make Today Great:

1) ....

2) ....

3) ....

Must-do's for the day?

....

....

....

Mid-Day Check-In

I am grateful for ....

Reflection

Anything about today that I would change?

....

....

....

Three Amazing things that happened today (big or small)?

1) ....

2) ....

3) ....

Projection

My desires/approach for tomorrow:

....

....

....

Date: ___ / ___ / ___

Intention:

Today I affirm:...

Three Things That Would Make Today Great:

1) ....

2) ....

3) ....

Must-do's for the day?

....

....

Mid-Day Check-In

I am grateful for ....

Reflection

Anything about today that I would change?

....

....

Three Amazing things that happened today (big or small)?

1) ....

2) ....

3) ....

Projection

My desires/approach for tomorrow:

....

....

Date:_____ / _____ / _____

Intention:

Today I affirm:..

Three Things That Would Make Today Great:

1) ....

2) ....

3) ....

Must-do's for the day?

....

....

Mid-Day Check-In

I am grateful for ....

Reflection

Anything about today that I would change?

....

....

....

Three Amazing things that happened today (big or small)?

1) ....

2) ....

3) ....

Projection

My desires/approach for tomorrow:

....

....

....

Date:____/____/____

Intention:

Today I affirm:...

Three Things That Would Make Today Great:

1) ....

2) ....

3) ....

Must-do's for the day?

....

....

Mid-Day Check-In

I am grateful for ....

Reflection

Anything about today that I would change?

....

....

....

Three Amazing things that happened today (big or small)?

1) ....

2) ....

3) ....

Projection

My desires/approach for tomorrow:

....

....

Date:___/___/___

Intention:

Today I affirm:..

Three Things That Would Make Today Great:

1) ....

2) ....

3) ....

Must-do's for the day?

....

....

Mid-Day Check-In

I am grateful for ....

Reflection

Anything about today that I would change?

....

....

....

Three Amazing things that happened today (big or small)?

1) ....

2) ....

3) ....

Projection

My desires/approach for tomorrow:

....

....

....

Date: ___/___/___

Intention:

Today I affirm:..

Three Things That Would Make Today Great:

1) ....

2) ....

3) ....

Must-do's for the day?

....

....

Mid-Day Check-In

I am grateful for ....

Reflection

Anything about today that I would change?

....

....

Three Amazing things that happened today (big or small)?

1) ....

2) ....

3) ....

Projection

My desires/approach for tomorrow:

....

....

Date: ___/___/___

Intention:

Today I affirm: ....

Three Things That Would Make Today Great:

1) ....

2) ....

3) ....

Must-do's for the day?

....

....

Mid-Day Check-In

I am grateful for ....

Reflection

Anything about today that I would change?

....

....

....

Three Amazing things that happened today (big or small)?

1) ....

2) ....

3) ....

Projection

My desires/approach for tomorrow:

....

....

....

Date: _____ / _____ / _____

Intention:

Today I affirm: ....

1) ....

2) ....

3) ....

Must-do's for the day?

....

....

Mid-Day Check-In

I am grateful for ....

Reflection

Anything about today that I would change?

....

....

Three Amazing things that happened today (big or small)?

1) ....

2) ....

3) ....

Projection

My desires/approach for tomorrow:

....

....

Date:____/____/____

Intention:

Today I affirm:...

Three Things That Would Make Today Great:

1) ....

2) ....

3) ....

Must-do's for the day?

....

....

Mid-Day Check-In

I am grateful for ....

Reflection

Anything about today that I would change?

....

....

....

Three Amazing things that happened today (big or small)?

1) ....

2) ....

3) ....

Projection

My desires/approach for tomorrow:

....

....

....

Date: ___/___/___

Intention:

Today I affirm:..

Three Things That Would Make Today Great:

1) ....

2) ....

3) ....

Must-do's for the day?

....

....

Mid-Day Check-In

I am grateful for ....

Reflection

Anything about today that I would change?

....

....

....

Three Amazing things that happened today (big or small)?

1) ....

2) ....

3) ....

Projection

My desires/approach for tomorrow:

....

....

Date: ___/___/___

Intention:

Today I affirm: ....

Three Things That Would Make Today Great:

1) ....

2) ....

3) ....

Must-do's for the day?

....

....

....

Mid-Day Check-In

I am grateful for ....

Reflection

Anything about today that I would change?

....

....

....

Three Amazing things that happened today (big or small)?

1) ....

2) ....

3) ....

Projection

My desires/approach for tomorrow:

....

....

....

Date: _____ / _____ / _____

Intention:

Today I affirm:..

Three Things That Would Make Today Great:

1) ....

2) ....

3) ....

Must-do's for the day?

....

....

Mid-Day Check-In

I am grateful for ....

Reflection

Anything about today that I would change?

....

....

Three Amazing things that happened today (big or small)?

1) ....

2) ....

3) ....

Projection

My desires/approach for tomorrow:

....

....

Date: ___ / ___ / ___

Intention:

Today I affirm: ....

Three Things That Would Make Today Great:

1) ....

2) ....

3) ....

Must-do's for the day?

....

....

....

Mid-Day Check-In

I am grateful for ....

Reflection

Anything about today that I would change?

....

....

....

Three Amazing things that happened today (big or small)?

1) ....

2) ....

3) ....

Projection

My desires/approach for tomorrow:

....

....

....

Date: ___/___/___

Intention:

Today I affirm:..

Three Things That Would Make Today Great:

1) ....

2) ....

3) ....

Must-do's for the day?

....

....

Mid-Day Check-In

I am grateful for ....

Reflection

Anything about today that I would change?

....

....

....

Three Amazing things that happened today (big or small)?

1) ....

2) ....

3) ....

Projection

My desires/approach for tomorrow:

....

....

Date: ___/___/___

Intention:

Today I affirm:...

Three Things That Would Make Today Great:

1) ....

2) ....

3) ....

Must-do's for the day?

....

....

Mid-Day Check-In

I am grateful for ....

Reflection

Anything about today that I would change?

....

....

....

Three Amazing things that happened today (big or small)?

1) ....

2) ....

3) ....

Projection

My desires/approach for tomorrow:

....

....

....

Date: ___ / ___ / ___

Intention:

Today I affirm: ....

Three Things That Would Make Today Great:

1) ....

2) ....

3) ....

Must-do's for the day?

....

....

Mid-Day Check-In

I am grateful for ....

Reflection

Anything about today that I would change?

....

....

Three Amazing things that happened today (big or small)?

1) ....

2) ....

3) ....

Projection

My desires/approach for tomorrow:

....

....

Date:____/____/____

Intention:

Today I affirm:..

Three Things That Would Make Today Great:

1) ....

2) ....

3) ....

Must-do's for the day?

....

....

Mid-Day Check-In

I am grateful for ....

Reflection

Anything about today that I would change?

....

....

....

Three Amazing things that happened today (big or small)?

1) ....

2) ....

3) ....

Projection

My desires/approach for tomorrow:

....

....

....

Date: ___/___/___

Intention:

Today I affirm: ....

Three Things That Would Make Today Great:

1) ....

2) ....

3) ....

Must-do's for the day?

....

....

Mid-Day Check-In

I am grateful for ....

Reflection

Anything about today that I would change?

....

....

Three Amazing things that happened today (big or small)?

1) ....

2) ....

3) ....

Projection

My desires/approach for tomorrow:

....

....

Date: ___/___/___

Intention:

Today I affirm: ....

Three Things That Would Make Today Great:

1) ....

2) ....

3) ....

Must-do's for the day?

....

....

....

Mid-Day Check-In

I am grateful for ....

Reflection

Anything about today that I would change?

....

....

....

Three Amazing things that happened today (big or small)?

1) ....

2) ....

3) ....

Projection

My desires/approach for tomorrow:

....

....

....

Date: ___/___/___

Intention:

Today I affirm:...

Three Things That Would Make Today Great:

1) ....

2) ....

3) ....

Must-do's for the day?

....

....

Mid-Day Check-In

I am grateful for ....

Reflection

Anything about today that I would change?

....

....

....

Three Amazing things that happened today (big or small)?

1) ....

2) ....

3) ....

Projection

My desires/approach for tomorrow:

....

....

....

Date:_____/_____/_____

Intention:

Today I affirm:...

Three Things That Would Make Today Great:

1) ....

2) ....

3) ....

Must-do's for the day?

....

....

Mid-Day Check-In

I am grateful for ....

Reflection

Anything about today that I would change?

....

....

....

Three Amazing things that happened today (big or small)?

1) ....

2) ....

3) ....

Projection

My desires/approach for tomorrow:

....

....

....

Date: ___ / ___ / ___

Intention:

Today I affirm:...

Three Things That Would Make Today Great:

1) ....

2) ....

3) ....

Must-do's for the day?

....

....

Mid-Day Check-In

I am grateful for ....

Reflection

Anything about today that I would change?

....

....

Three Amazing things that happened today (big or small)?

1) ....

2) ....

3) ....

Projection

My desires/approach for tomorrow:

....

....

Date:_____/_____/_____

Intention:

Today I affirm:..

Three Things That Would Make Today Great:

1) ....

2) ....

3) ....

Must-do's for the day?

....

....

Mid-Day Check-In

I am grateful for ....

Reflection

Anything about today that I would change?

....

....

....

Three Amazing things that happened today (big or small)?

1) ....

2) ....

3) ....

Projection

My desires/approach for tomorrow:

....

....

....

Date: ___ / ___ / ___

Intention:

Today I affirm:..

Three Things That Would Make Today Great:

1) ....

2) ....

3) ....

Must-do's for the day?

....

....

Mid-Day Check-In

I am grateful for ....

Reflection

Anything about today that I would change?

....

....

Three Amazing things that happened today (big or small)?

1) ....

2) ....

3) ....

Projection

My desires/approach for tomorrow:

....

....

Date:_____/_____/_____

Intention:

Today I affirm:...

Three Things That Would Make Today Great:

1) ....

2) ....

3) ....

Must-do's for the day?

....

....

Mid-Day Check-In

I am grateful for...

Reflection

Anything about today that I would change?

....

....

....

Three Amazing things that happened today (big or small)?

1) ....

2) ....

3) ....

Projection

My desires/approach for tomorrow:

....

....

....

Date: ___/___/___

Intention:

Today I affirm:...

Three Things That Would Make Today Great:

1) ....

2) ....

3) ....

Must-do's for the day?

....

....

Mid-Day Check-In

I am grateful for ....

Reflection

Anything about today that I would change?

....

....

....

Three Amazing things that happened today (big or small)?

1) ....

2) ....

3) ....

Projection

My desires/approach for tomorrow:

....

....

Date:___/___/___

Intention:

Today I affirm:...

Three Things That Would Make Today Great:

1) ....

2) ....

3) ....

Must-do's for the day?

....

....

Mid-Day Check-In

I am grateful for ....

Reflection

Anything about today that I would change?

....

....

....

Three Amazing things that happened today (big or small)?

1) ....

2) ....

3) ....

Projection

My desires/approach for tomorrow:

....

....

....

Date: ___/___/___

Intention:

Today I affirm:...

1) ....

2) ....

3) ....

Must-do's for the day?

....

....

Mid-Day Check-In

I am grateful for ....

Reflection

Anything about today that I would change?

....

....

Three Amazing things that happened today (big or small)?

1) ....

2) ....

3) ....

Projection

My desires/approach for tomorrow:

....

....

Date:____/____/____

Intention:

Today I affirm:..

Three Things That Would Make Today Great:

1) ....

2) ....

3) ....

Must-do's for the day?

....

....

Mid-Day Check-In

I am grateful for ....

Reflection

Anything about today that I would change?

....

....

....

Three Amazing things that happened today (big or small)?

1) ....

2) ....

3) ....

Projection

My desires/approach for tomorrow:

....

....

....

Date: ___/___/___

Intention:

Today I affirm:...

Three Things That Would Make Today Great:

1) ....

2) ....

3) ....

Must-do's for the day?

....

....

Mid-Day Check-In

I am grateful for ....

Reflection

Anything about today that I would change?

....

....

Three Amazing things that happened today (big or small)?

1) ....

2) ....

3) ....

Projection

My desires/approach for tomorrow:

....

....

Date:_____/_____/_____

Intention:

Today I affirm:..

Three Things That Would Make Today Great:

1) ....

2) ....

3) ....

Must-do's for the day?

....

....

Mid-Day Check-In

I am grateful for ....

Reflection

Anything about today that I would change?

....

....

....

Three Amazing things that happened today (big or small)?

1) ....

2) ....

3) ....

Projection

My desires/approach for tomorrow:

....

....

....

Date: ___/___/___

Intention:

Today I affirm:..

Three Things That Would Make Today Great:

1) ....

2) ....

3) ....

Must-do's for the day?

....

....

Mid-Day Check-In

I am grateful for ....

Reflection

Anything about today that I would change?

....

....

Three Amazing things that happened today (big or small)?

1) ....

2) ....

3) ....

Projection

My desires/approach for tomorrow:

....

....

Date:____/____/____

Intention:

Today I affirm:...

Three Things That Would Make Today Great:

1) ....

2) ....

3) ....

Must-do's for the day?

....

....

....

Mid-Day Check-In

I am grateful for ....

Reflection

Anything about today that I would change?

....

....

....

Three Amazing things that happened today (big or small)?

1) ....

2) ....

3) ....

Projection

My desires/approach for tomorrow:

....

....

....

Date: ___ / ___ / ___

Intention:

Today I affirm: ....

Three Things That Would Make Today Great:

1) ....

2) ....

3) ....

Must-do's for the day?

....

....

....

Mid-Day Check-In

I am grateful for ....

Reflection

Anything about today that I would change?

....

....

....

Three Amazing things that happened today (big or small)?

1) ....

2) ....

3) ....

Projection

My desires/approach for tomorrow:

....

....

Date:_____/_____/_____

Intention:

Today I affirm:...

Three Things That Would Make Today Great:

1) ....

2) ....

3) ....

Must-do's for the day?

....

....

Mid-Day Check-In

I am grateful for ....

Reflection

Anything about today that I would change?

....

....

....

Three Amazing things that happened today (big or small)?

1) ....

2) ....

3) ....

Projection

My desires/approach for tomorrow:

....

....

....

Date: ___ / ___ / ___

Intention:

Today I affirm:...

Three Things That Would Make Today Great:

1) ....

2) ....

3) ....

Must-do's for the day?

....

....

Mid-Day Check-In

I am grateful for ....

Reflection

Anything about today that I would change?

....

....

Three Amazing things that happened today (big or small)?

1) ....

2) ....

3) ....

Projection

My desires/approach for tomorrow:

....

....

Date:_____/_____/_____

Intention:

Today I affirm:...

Three Things That Would Make Today Great:

1) ....

2) ....

3) ....

Must-do's for the day?

....

....

Mid-Day Check-In

I am grateful for ....

Reflection

Anything about today that I would change?

....

....

....

Three Amazing things that happened today (big or small)?

1) ....

2) ....

3) ....

Projection

My desires/approach for tomorrow:

....

....

....

Date: ___ / ___ / ___

Intention:

Today I affirm:..

Three Things That Would Make Today Great:

1) ....

2) ....

3) ....

Must-do's for the day?

....

....

Mid-Day Check-In

I am grateful for ....

Reflection

Anything about today that I would change?

....

....

Three Amazing things that happened today (big or small)?

1) ....

2) ....

3) ....

Projection

My desires/approach for tomorrow:

....

....

Date: ___/___/___

Intention:

Today I affirm:..

Three Things That Would Make Today Great:

1) ....

2) ....

3) ....

Must-do's for the day?

....

....

Mid-Day Check-In

I am grateful for ....

Reflection

Anything about today that I would change?

....

....

....

Three Amazing things that happened today (big or small)?

1) ....

2) ....

3) ....

Projection

My desires/approach for tomorrow:

....

....

....

Date: ___ / ___ / ___

Intention:

Today I affirm: ....

Three Things That Would Make Today Great:

1) ....

2) ....

3) ....

Must-do's for the day?

....

....

Mid-Day Check-In

I am grateful for ....

Reflection

Anything about today that I would change?

....

....

Three Amazing things that happened today (big or small)?

1) ....

2) ....

3) ....

Projection

My desires/approach for tomorrow:

....

....

Date:_____/_____/_____

Intention:

Today I affirm:...

Three Things That Would Make Today Great:

1) ....

2) ....

3) ....

Must-do's for the day?

....

....

....

Mid-Day Check-In

I am grateful for ....

Reflection

Anything about today that I would change?

....

....

....

Three Amazing things that happened today (big or small)?

1) ....

2) ....

3) ....

Projection

My desires/approach for tomorrow:

....

....

Date: ___/___/___

Intention:

Today I affirm:...

Three Things That Would Make Today Great:

1) ....

2) ....

3) ....

Must-do's for the day?

....

....

....

Mid-Day Check-In

I am grateful for ....

Reflection

Anything about today that I would change?

....

....

....

Three Amazing things that happened today (big or small)?

1) ....

2) ....

3) ....

Projection

My desires/approach for tomorrow:

....

....

....

Date:_____/_____/_____

Intention:

Today I affirm:...

Three Things That Would Make Today Great:

1) ....

2) ....

3) ....

Must-do's for the day?

....

....

....

Mid-Day Check-In

I am grateful for ....

Reflection

Anything about today that I would change?

....

....

....

Three Amazing things that happened today (big or small)?

1) ....

2) ....

3) ....

Projection

My desires/approach for tomorrow:

....

....

....

Date: ___ / ___ / ___

Intention:

Today I affirm: ....

Three Things That Would Make Today Great:

1) ....

2) ....

3) ....

Must-do's for the day?

....

....

Mid-Day Check-In

I am grateful for ....

Reflection

Anything about today that I would change?

....

....

Three Amazing things that happened today (big or small)?

1) ....

2) ....

3) ....

Projection

My desires/approach for tomorrow:

....

....

Date:_____/_____/_____

Intention:

Today I affirm:..

1) ....

2) ....

3) ....

Must-do's for the day?

....

....

Mid-Day Check-In

I am grateful for ....

Reflection

Anything about today that I would change?

....

....

....

Three Amazing things that happened today (big or small)?

1) ....

2) ....

3) ....

Projection

My desires/approach for tomorrow:

....

....

....

Date: ___/___/___

Intention:

Today I affirm:_____

Three Things That Would Make Today Great:

1) _____

2) _____

3) _____

Must-do's for the day?

_____

_____

Mid-Day Check-In

I am grateful for _____

Reflection

Anything about today that I would change?

_____

_____

Three Amazing things that happened today (big or small)?

1) _____

2) _____

3) _____

Projection

My desires/approach for tomorrow:

_____

_____

Date:_____/_____/_____

Intention:

Today I affirm:..

1) ....

2) ....

3) ....

Must-do's for the day?

Mid-Day Check-In

I am grateful for ....

Reflection

Anything about today that I would change?

Three Amazing things that happened today (big or small)?

1) ....

2) ....

3) ....

Projection

My desires/approach for tomorrow:

Date:_____/_____/_____

Intention:

Today I affirm:..

Three Things That Would Make Today Great:

1) ....

2) ....

3) ....

Must-do's for the day?

....

....

Mid-Day Check-In

I am grateful for ....

Reflection

Anything about today that I would change?

....

....

Three Amazing things that happened today (big or small)?

1) ....

2) ....

3) ....

Projection

My desires/approach for tomorrow:

....

....

Date:_____/_____/_____

Intention:

Today I affirm:..

Three Things That Would Make Today Great:

1) ....

2) ....

3) ....

Must-do's for the day?

....

....

Mid-Day Check-In

I am grateful for ....

Reflection

Anything about today that I would change?

....

....

....

Three Amazing things that happened today (big or small)?

1) ....

2) ....

3) ....

Projection

My desires/approach for tomorrow:

....

....

....

Date:_____/_____/_____

Intention:

Today I affirm:..

Three Things That Would Make Today Great:

1) ....

2) ....

3) ....

Must-do's for the day?

....

....

Mid-Day Check-In

I am grateful for ....

Reflection

Anything about today that I would change?

....

....

Three Amazing things that happened today (big or small)?

1) ....

2) ....

3) ....

Projection

My desires/approach for tomorrow:

....

....

Date: _____ / _____ / _____

Intention:

Today I affirm: ....

Three Things That Would Make Today Great:

1) ....

2) ....

3) ....

Must-do's for the day?

....

....

Mid-Day Check-In

I am grateful for ....

Reflection

Anything about today that I would change?

....

....

....

Three Amazing things that happened today (big or small)?

1) ....

2) ....

3) ....

Projection

My desires/approach for tomorrow:

....

....

....

Date: ___ / ___ / ___

Intention:

Today I affirm:..

Three Things That Would Make Today Great:

1) ....

2) ....

3) ....

Must-do's for the day?

....

....

Mid-Day Check-In

I am grateful for ....

Reflection

Anything about today that I would change?

....

....

Three Amazing things that happened today (big or small)?

1) ....

2) ....

3) ....

Projection

My desires/approach for tomorrow:

....

....

Date:_____/_____/_____

Intention:

Today I affirm:...

Three Things That Would Make Today Great:

1) ....

2) ....

3) ....

Must-do's for the day?

....

....

Mid-Day Check-In

I am grateful for ....

Reflection

Anything about today that I would change?

....

....

....

Three Amazing things that happened today (big or small)?

1) ....

2) ....

3) ....

Projection

My desires/approach for tomorrow:

....

....

....

Date: ___/___/___

Intention:

Today I affirm:...

Three Things That Would Make Today Great:

1) ....
2) ....
3) ....

Must-do's for the day?

....

....

....

Mid-Day Check-In

I am grateful for ....

Reflection

Anything about today that I would change?

....

....

....

Three Amazing things that happened today (big or small)?

1) ....
2) ....
3) ....

Projection

My desires/approach for tomorrow:

....

....

....

Date: ___ / ___ / ___

Intention:

Today I affirm: ....

Three Things That Would Make Today Great:

1) ....

2) ....

3) ....

Must-do's for the day?

....

....

Mid-Day Check-In

I am grateful for ....

Reflection

Anything about today that I would change?

....

....

....

Three Amazing things that happened today (big or small)?

1) ....

2) ....

3) ....

Projection

My desires/approach for tomorrow:

....

....

Date: ___ / ___ / ___

Intention:

Today I affirm:...

Three Things That Would Make Today Great:

1) ....

2) ....

3) ....

Must-do's for the day?

....

....

Mid-Day Check-In

I am grateful for ....

Reflection

Anything about today that I would change?

....

....

Three Amazing things that happened today (big or small)?

1) ....

2) ....

3) ....

Projection

My desires/approach for tomorrow:

....

....

Date: ___/___/___

Intention:

Today I affirm: ....

Three Things That Would Make Today Great:

1) ....

2) ....

3) ....

Must-do's for the day?

....

....

Mid-Day Check-In

I am grateful for ....

Reflection

Anything about today that I would change?

....

....

....

Three Amazing things that happened today (big or small)?

1) ....

2) ....

3) ....

Projection

My desires/approach for tomorrow:

....

....

....

Date: ___/___/___

Intention:

Today I affirm:...

Three Things That Would Make Today Great:

1) ....

2) ....

3) ....

Must-do's for the day?

....

....

....

Mid-Day Check-In

I am grateful for ....

Reflection

Anything about today that I would change?

....

....

....

Three Amazing things that happened today (big or small)?

1) ....

2) ....

3) ....

Projection

My desires/approach for tomorrow:

....

....

....

Date:____/____/____

Intention:

Today I affirm:..

Three Things That Would Make Today Great:

1) ....

2) ....

3) ....

Must-do's for the day?

....

....

Mid-Day Check-In

I am grateful for ....

Reflection

Anything about today that I would change?

....

....

....

Three Amazing things that happened today (big or small)?

1) ....

2) ....

3) ....

Projection

My desires/approach for tomorrow:

....

....

....

Date: ___/___/___

Intention:

Today I affirm:...

Three Things That Would Make Today Great:

1) ....

2) ....

3) ....

Must-do's for the day?

....

....

Mid-Day Check-In

I am grateful for ....

Reflection

Anything about today that I would change?

....

....

Three Amazing things that happened today (big or small)?

1) ....

2) ....

3) ....

Projection

My desires/approach for tomorrow:

....

....

Date:_____/_____/_____

Intention:

Today I affirm:...

Three Things That Would Make Today Great:

1) ....

2) ....

3) ....

Must-do's for the day?

....

....

Mid-Day Check-In

I am grateful for ....

Reflection

Anything about today that I would change?

....

....

....

Three Amazing things that happened today (big or small)?

1) ....

2) ....

3) ....

Projection

My desires/approach for tomorrow:

....

....

....

Date: ___/___/___

Intention:

Today I affirm: ....

Three Things That Would Make Today Great:

1) ....

2) ....

3) ....

Must-do's for the day?

....

....

....

Mid-Day Check-In

I am grateful for ....

Reflection

Anything about today that I would change?

....

....

....

Three Amazing things that happened today (big or small)?

1) ....

2) ....

3) ....

Projection

My desires/approach for tomorrow:

....

....

....

Date:_____ /_____ /_____

Intention:

Today I affirm:...

Three Things That Would Make Today Great:

1) ....

2) ....

3) ....

Must-do's for the day?

....

....

Mid-Day Check-In

I am grateful for ....

Reflection

Anything about today that I would change?

....

....

....

Three Amazing things that happened today (big or small)?

1) ....

2) ....

3) ....

Projection

My desires/approach for tomorrow:

....

....

....

Date: ___ / ___ / ___

Intention:

Today I affirm:...

Three Things That Would Make Today Great:

1) ....

2) ....

3) ....

Must-do's for the day?

....

....

Mid-Day Check-In

I am grateful for ....

Reflection

Anything about today that I would change?

....

....

Three Amazing things that happened today (big or small)?

1) ....

2) ....

3) ....

Projection

My desires/approach for tomorrow:

....

....

Date: ___/___/___

Intention:

Today I affirm:..

Three Things That Would Make Today Great:

1) ....

2) ....

3) ....

Must-do's for the day?

....

....

Mid-Day Check-In

I am grateful for ....

Reflection

Anything about today that I would change?

....

....

....

Three Amazing things that happened today (big or small)?

1) ....

2) ....

3) ....

Projection

My desires/approach for tomorrow:

....

....

....

Date:___/___/___

Intention:

Today I affirm:..

Three Things That Would Make Today Great:

1) ....

2) ....

3) ....

Must-do's for the day?

....

....

....

Mid-Day Check-In

I am grateful for ....

Reflection

Anything about today that I would change?

....

....

....

Three Amazing things that happened today (big or small)?

1) ....

2) ....

3) ....

Projection

My desires/approach for tomorrow:

....

....

....

Date:_____/_____/_____

Intention:

Today I affirm:..

Three Things That Would Make Today Great:

1) ....

2) ....

3) ....

Must-do's for the day?

....

....

....

Mid-Day Check-In

I am grateful for ....

Reflection

Anything about today that I would change?

....

....

....

Three Amazing things that happened today (big or small)?

1) ....

2) ....

3) ....

Projection

My desires/approach for tomorrow:

....

....

....

Date: ___/___/___

Intention:

Today I affirm:...

Three Things That Would Make Today Great:

1) ....

2) ....

3) ....

Must-do's for the day?

....

....

Mid-Day Check-In

I am grateful for ....

Reflection

Anything about today that I would change?

....

....

Three Amazing things that happened today (big or small)?

1) ....

2) ....

3) ....

Projection

My desires/approach for tomorrow:

....

....

Date: _____/_____/_____

Intention:

Today I affirm:...

1) ....

2) ....

3) ....

Must-do's for the day?

....

....

Mid-Day Check-In

I am grateful for ....

Reflection

Anything about today that I would change?

....

....

Three Amazing things that happened today (big or small)?

1) ....

2) ....

3) ....

Projection

My desires/approach for tomorrow:

....

....

Date:_____/_____/_____

Intention:

Today I affirm:...

Three Things That Would Make Today Great:

1) ....

2) ....

3) ....

Must-do's for the day?

....

....

Mid-Day Check-In

I am grateful for ....

Reflection

Anything about today that I would change?

....

....

....

Three Amazing things that happened today (big or small)?

1) ....

2) ....

3) ....

Projection

My desires/approach for tomorrow:

....

....

....

Date: _____ / _____ / _____

Intention:

Today I affirm: ....

Three Things That Would Make Today Great:

1) ....

2) ....

3) ....

Must-do's for the day?

....

....

Mid-Day Check-In

I am grateful for ....

Reflection

Anything about today that I would change?

....

....

....

Three Amazing things that happened today (big or small)?

1) ....

2) ....

3) ....

Projection

My desires/approach for tomorrow:

....

....

....

Date: ___ / ___ / ___

Intention:

Today I affirm: ....

Three Things That Would Make Today Great:

1) ....

2) ....

3) ....

Must-do's for the day?

....

....

Mid-Day Check-In

I am grateful for ....

Reflection

Anything about today that I would change?

....

....

Three Amazing things that happened today (big or small)?

1) ....

2) ....

3) ....

Projection

My desires/approach for tomorrow:

....

....

....

Date: ___/___/___

Intention:

Today I affirm:...

Three Things That Would Make Today Great:

1) ....

2) ....

3) ....

Must-do's for the day?

....

....

Mid-Day Check-In

I am grateful for ....

Reflection

Anything about today that I would change?

....

....

....

Three Amazing things that happened today (big or small)?

1) ....

2) ....

3) ....

Projection

My desires/approach for tomorrow:

....

....

....

Date: ___ / ___ / ___

Intention:

Today I affirm:...

Three Things That Would Make Today Great:

1) ....

2) ....

3) ....

Must-do's for the day?

....

....

Mid-Day Check-In

I am grateful for ....

Reflection

Anything about today that I would change?

....

....

Three Amazing things that happened today (big or small)?

1) ....

2) ....

3) ....

Projection

My desires/approach for tomorrow:

....

....

Date:_____/_____/_____

Intention:

Today I affirm:..

Three Things That Would Make Today Great:

1) ....

2) ....

3) ....

Must-do's for the day?

....

....

....

Mid-Day Check-In

I am grateful for ....

Reflection

Anything about today that I would change?

....

....

....

Three Amazing things that happened today (big or small)?

1) ....

2) ....

3) ....

Projection

My desires/approach for tomorrow:

....

....

....

Date: ___ / ___ / ___

Intention:

Today I affirm: ....

Three Things That Would Make Today Great:

1) ....

2) ....

3) ....

Must-do's for the day?

....

....

Mid-Day Check-In

I am grateful for ....

Reflection

Anything about today that I would change?

....

....

....

Three Amazing things that happened today (big or small)?

1) ....

2) ....

3) ....

Projection

My desires/approach for tomorrow:

....

....

Date:____/____/____

Intention:

Today I affirm:..

Three Things That Would Make Today Great:

1) ....

2) ....

3) ....

Must-do's for the day?

....

....

....

Mid-Day Check-In

I am grateful for..

Reflection

Anything about today that I would change?

....

....

....

Three Amazing things that happened today (big or small)?

1) ....

2) ....

3) ....

Projection

My desires/approach for tomorrow:

....

....

....

Date: ___/___/___

Intention:

Today I affirm: ....

Three Things That Would Make Today Great:

1) ....

2) ....

3) ....

Must-do's for the day?

....

....

Mid-Day Check-In

I am grateful for ....

Reflection

Anything about today that I would change?

....

....

Three Amazing things that happened today (big or small)?

1) ....

2) ....

3) ....

Projection

My desires/approach for tomorrow:

....

....

Date:___/___/___

Intention:

Today I affirm:...

Three Things That Would Make Today Great:

1) ....

2) ....

3) ....

Must-do's for the day?

....

....

Mid-Day Check-In

I am grateful for ....

Reflection

Anything about today that I would change?

....

....

....

Three Amazing things that happened today (big or small)?

1) ....

2) ....

3) ....

Projection

My desires/approach for tomorrow:

....

....

....

Date:___/___/___

Intention:

Today I affirm:...

Three Things That Would Make Today Great:

1) ....

2) ....

3) ....

Must-do's for the day?

....

....

Mid-Day Check-In

I am grateful for ....

Reflection

Anything about today that I would change?

....

....

Three Amazing things that happened today (big or small)?

1) ....

2) ....

3) ....

Projection

My desires/approach for tomorrow:

....

....

....

Date: _____/_____/_____

Intention:

Today I affirm:...

Three Things That Would Make Today Great:

1) ....

2) ....

3) ....

Must-do's for the day?

....

....

Mid-Day Check-In

I am grateful for ....

Reflection

Anything about today that I would change?

....

....

....

Three Amazing things that happened today (big or small)?

1) ....

2) ....

3) ....

Projection

My desires/approach for tomorrow:

....

....

....

Date: ___/___/___

Intention:

Today I affirm:...

Three Things That Would Make Today Great:

1) ....

2) ....

3) ....

Must-do's for the day?

....

....

Mid-Day Check-In

I am grateful for ....

Reflection

Anything about today that I would change?

....

....

....

Three Amazing things that happened today (big or small)?

1) ....

2) ....

3) ....

Projection

My desires/approach for tomorrow:

....

....

....

Date: ___/___/___

Intention:

Today I affirm: ....

Three Things That Would Make Today Great:

1) ....

2) ....

3) ....

Must-do's for the day?

....

....

Mid-Day Check-In

I am grateful for ....

Reflection

Anything about today that I would change?

....

....

Three Amazing things that happened today (big or small)?

1) ....

2) ....

3) ....

Projection

My desires/approach for tomorrow:

....

....

Date: ___ / ___ / ___

Intention:

Today I affirm:...

Three Things That Would Make Today Great:

1) ....

2) ....

3) ....

Must-do's for the day?

....

....

Mid-Day Check-In

I am grateful for ....

Reflection

Anything about today that I would change?

....

....

Three Amazing things that happened today (big or small)?

1) ....

2) ....

3) ....

Projection

My desires/approach for tomorrow:

....

....

Date: ___/___/___

Intention:

Today I affirm: ....

Three Things That Would Make Today Great:

1) ....

2) ....

3) ....

Must-do's for the day?

....

....

Mid-Day Check-In

I am grateful for ....

Reflection

Anything about today that I would change?

....

....

....

Three Amazing things that happened today (big or small)?

1) ....

2) ....

3) ....

Projection

My desires/approach for tomorrow:

....

....

....

Date:_____/_____/_____

Intention:

Today I affirm:...

Three Things That Would Make Today Great:

1) ....

2) ....

3) ....

Must-do's for the day?

....

....

Mid-Day Check-In

I am grateful for ....

Reflection

Anything about today that I would change?

....

....

Three Amazing things that happened today (big or small)?

1) ....

2) ....

3) ....

Projection

My desires/approach for tomorrow:

....

....

Date: ___/___/___

Intention:

Today I affirm:...

Three Things That Would Make Today Great:

1) ....

2) ....

3) ....

Must-do's for the day?

....

....

Mid-Day Check-In

I am grateful for ....

Reflection

Anything about today that I would change?

....

....

....

Three Amazing things that happened today (big or small)?

1) ....

2) ....

3) ....

Projection

My desires/approach for tomorrow:

....

....

Date: ___/___/___

Intention:

Today I affirm: ....

Three Things That Would Make Today Great:

1) ....

2) ....

3) ....

Must-do's for the day?

....

....

Mid-Day Check-In

I am grateful for ....

Reflection

Anything about today that I would change?

....

....

....

Three Amazing things that happened today (big or small)?

1) ....

2) ....

3) ....

Projection

My desires/approach for tomorrow:

....

....

....

Date:____/____/____

Intention:

Today I affirm:..

Three Things That Would Make Today Great:

1) ....

2) ....

3) ....

Must-do's for the day?

....

....

Mid-Day Check-In

I am grateful for ....

Reflection

Anything about today that I would change?

....

....

....

Three Amazing things that happened today (big or small)?

1) ....

2) ....

3) ....

Projection

My desires/approach for tomorrow:

....

....

....

Date: ___/___/___

Intention:

Today I affirm:..

Three Things That Would Make Today Great:

1) ....

2) ....

3) ....

Must-do's for the day?

....

....

Mid-Day Check-In

I am grateful for ....

Reflection

Anything about today that I would change?

....

....

Three Amazing things that happened today (big or small)?

1) ....

2) ....

3) ....

Projection

My desires/approach for tomorrow:

....

....

....

Date: ___ / ___ / ___

Intention:

Today I affirm:...

Three Things That Would Make Today Great:

1) ....

2) ....

3) ....

Must-do's for the day?

....

....

....

Mid-Day Check-In

I am grateful for ....

Reflection

Anything about today that I would change?

....

....

....

Three Amazing things that happened today (big or small)?

1) ....

2) ....

3) ....

Projection

My desires/approach for tomorrow:

....

....

....

Date: ___ / ___ / ___

Intention:

Today I affirm:..

Three Things That Would Make Today Great:

1) ....

2) ....

3) ....

Must-do's for the day?

....

....

Mid-Day Check-In

I am grateful for ....

Reflection

Anything about today that I would change?

....

....

Three Amazing things that happened today (big or small)?

1) ....

2) ....

3) ....

Projection

My desires/approach for tomorrow:

....

....

Date: ___ / ___ / ___

Intention:

Today I affirm: ....

Three Things That Would Make Today Great:

1) ....

2) ....

3) ....

Must-do's for the day?

....

....

Mid-Day Check-In

I am grateful for ....

Reflection

Anything about today that I would change?

....

....

....

Three Amazing things that happened today (big or small)?

1) ....

2) ....

3) ....

Projection

My desires/approach for tomorrow:

....

....

....

Date: ___/___/___

Intention:

Today I affirm:...

Three Things That Would Make Today Great:

1) ....

2) ....

3) ....

Must-do's for the day?

....

....

Mid-Day Check-In

I am grateful for ....

Reflection

Anything about today that I would change?

....

....

Three Amazing things that happened today (big or small)?

1) ....

2) ....

3) ....

Projection

My desires/approach for tomorrow:

....

....

....

Date: _____/_____/_____

Intention:

Today I affirm:..

Three Things That Would Make Today Great:

1) ....

2) ....

3) ....

Must-do's for the day?

....

....

Mid-Day Check-In

I am grateful for ....

Reflection

Anything about today that I would change?

....

....

Three Amazing things that happened today (big or small)?

1) ....

2) ....

3) ....

Projection

My desires/approach for tomorrow:

....

....

Date:_____/_____/_____

Intention:

Today I affirm:..

1) ....

2) ....

3) ....

Must-do's for the day?

....

....

....

Mid-Day Check-In

I am grateful for ....

Reflection

Anything about today that I would change?

....

....

....

Three Amazing things that happened today (big or small)?

1) ....

2) ....

3) ....

Projection

My desires/approach for tomorrow:

....

....

....

Date: ___/___/___

Intention:

Today I affirm: ....

Three Things That Would Make Today Great:

1) ....

2) ....

3) ....

Must-do's for the day?

....

....

Mid-Day Check-In

I am grateful for ....

Reflection

Anything about today that I would change?

....

....

....

Three Amazing things that happened today (big or small)?

1) ....

2) ....

3) ....

Projection

My desires/approach for tomorrow:

....

....

Date: ___ / ___ / ___

Intention:

Today I affirm:...

Three Things That Would Make Today Great:

1) ....

2) ....

3) ....

Must-do's for the day?

....

....

Mid-Day Check-In

I am grateful for ....

Reflection

Anything about today that I would change?

....

....

....

Three Amazing things that happened today (big or small)?

1) ....

2) ....

3) ....

Projection

My desires/approach for tomorrow:

....

....

....

Date:___/___/___

Intention:

Today I affirm:...

Three Things That Would Make Today Great:

1) ....

2) ....

3) ....

Must-do's for the day?

....

....

Mid-Day Check-In

I am grateful for ....

Reflection

Anything about today that I would change?

....

....

....

Three Amazing things that happened today (big or small)?

1) ....

2) ....

3) ....

Projection

My desires/approach for tomorrow:

....

....

....

Date: ___ / ___ / ___

Intention:

Today I affirm:..

Three Things That Would Make Today Great:

1) ....

2) ....

3) ....

Must-do's for the day?

....

....

Mid-Day Check-In

I am grateful for ....

Reflection

Anything about today that I would change?

....

....

Three Amazing things that happened today (big or small)?

1) ....

2) ....

3) ....

Projection

My desires/approach for tomorrow:

....

....

Date:___/___/___

Intention:

Today I affirm:..

Three Things That Would Make Today Great:

1) ....

2) ....

3) ....

Must-do's for the day?

....

....

Mid-Day Check-In

I am grateful for ....

Reflection

Anything about today that I would change?

....

....

....

Three Amazing things that happened today (big or small)?

1) ....

2) ....

3) ....

Projection

My desires/approach for tomorrow:

....

....

....

Date:_____/_____/_____

Intention:

Today I affirm:...

Three Things That Would Make Today Great:

1) ....

2) ....

3) ....

Must-do's for the day?

....

....

Mid-Day Check-In

I am grateful for ....

Reflection

Anything about today that I would change?

....

....

....

Three Amazing things that happened today (big or small)?

1) ....

2) ....

3) ....

Projection

My desires/approach for tomorrow:

....

....

....

Date: ___ / ___ / ___

Intention:

Today I affirm: ....

Three Things That Would Make Today Great:

1) ....

2) ....

3) ....

Must-do's for the day?

....

....

Mid-Day Check-In

I am grateful for ....

Reflection

Anything about today that I would change?

....

....

....

Three Amazing things that happened today (big or small)?

1) ....

2) ....

3) ....

Projection

My desires/approach for tomorrow:

....

....

....

Date: ____ / ____ / ____

Intention:

Today I affirm:...

Three Things That Would Make Today Great:

1) ....

2) ....

3) ....

Must-do's for the day?

....

....

Mid-Day Check-In

I am grateful for ....

Reflection

Anything about today that I would change?

....

....

....

Three Amazing things that happened today (big or small)?

1) ....

2) ....

3) ....

Projection

My desires/approach for tomorrow:

....

....

....

Date: ___/___/___

Intention:

Today I affirm:..

Three Things That Would Make Today Great:

1) ....

2) ....

3) ....

Must-do's for the day?

....

....

....

Mid-Day Check-In

I am grateful for ....

Reflection

Anything about today that I would change?

....

....

....

Three Amazing things that happened today (big or small)?

1) ....

2) ....

3) ....

Projection

My desires/approach for tomorrow:

....

....

....

Date:___/___/___

Intention:

Today I affirm:_____

Three Things That Would Make Today Great:

1) _____

2) _____

3) _____

Must-do's for the day?

_____

_____

Mid-Day Check-In

I am grateful for _____

Reflection

Anything about today that I would change?

_____

_____

Three Amazing things that happened today (big or small)?

1) _____

2) _____

3) _____

Projection

My desires/approach for tomorrow:

_____

_____

Date: ___ / ___ / ___

Intention:

Today I affirm:...

Three Things That Would Make Today Great:

1) ....

2) ....

3) ....

Must-do's for the day?

....

....

....

Mid-Day Check-In

I am grateful for ....

Reflection

Anything about today that I would change?

....

....

....

Three Amazing things that happened today (big or small)?

1) ....

2) ....

3) ....

Projection

My desires/approach for tomorrow:

....

....

....

Date: ___/___/___

Intention:

Today I affirm:..

Three Things That Would Make Today Great:

1) ....

2) ....

3) ....

Must-do's for the day?

....

....

....

Mid-Day Check-In

I am grateful for ....

Reflection

Anything about today that I would change?

....

....

....

Three Amazing things that happened today (big or small)?

1) ....

2) ....

3) ....

Projection

My desires/approach for tomorrow:

....

....

....

Date:_____/_____/_____

Intention:

Today I affirm:..

Three Things That Would Make Today Great:

1) ....

2) ....

3) ....

Must-do's for the day?

....

....

....

Mid-Day Check-In

I am grateful for ....

Reflection

Anything about today that I would change?

....

....

....

Three Amazing things that happened today (big or small)?

1) ....

2) ....

3) ....

Projection

My desires/approach for tomorrow:

....

....

....

Date: ___/___/___

Intention:

Today I affirm:..

Three Things That Would Make Today Great:

1) ....

2) ....

3) ....

Must-do's for the day?

....

....

Mid-Day Check-In

I am grateful for ....

Reflection

Anything about today that I would change?

....

....

Three Amazing things that happened today (big or small)?

1) ....

2) ....

3) ....

Projection

My desires/approach for tomorrow:

....

....

Date: ___ / ___ / ___

Intention:

Today I affirm:..

Three Things That Would Make Today Great:

1) ....

2) ....

3) ....

Must-do's for the day?

....

....

Mid-Day Check-In

I am grateful for ....

Reflection

Anything about today that I would change?

....

....

....

Three Amazing things that happened today (big or small)?

1) ....

2) ....

3) ....

Projection

My desires/approach for tomorrow:

....

....

....

Date: ___ / ___ / ___

Intention:

Today I affirm:

Three Things That Would Make Today Great:

1)

2)

3)

Must-do's for the day?

Mid-Day Check-In

I am grateful for

Reflection

Anything about today that I would change?

Three Amazing things that happened today (big or small)?

1)

2)

3)

Projection

My desires/approach for tomorrow:

Date:____/____/____

Intention:

Today I affirm:...

Three Things That Would Make Today Great:

1) ....
2) ....
3) ....

Must-do's for the day?

....

....

....

Mid-Day Check-In

I am grateful for ....

Reflection

Anything about today that I would change?

....

....

....

Three Amazing things that happened today (big or small)?

1) ....
2) ....
3) ....

Projection

My desires/approach for tomorrow:

....

....

....

Date: ___/___/___

Intention:

Today I affirm:...

Three Things That Would Make Today Great:

1) ....

2) ....

3) ....

Must-do's for the day?

....

....

Mid-Day Check-In

I am grateful for ....

Reflection

Anything about today that I would change?

....

....

....

Three Amazing things that happened today (big or small)?

1) ....

2) ....

3) ....

Projection

My desires/approach for tomorrow:

....

....

....

Date:_____/_____/_____

Intention:

Today I affirm:..

Three Things That Would Make Today Great:

1) ....

2) ....

3) ....

Must-do's for the day?

....

....

Mid-Day Check-In

I am grateful for ....

Reflection

Anything about today that I would change?

....

....

....

Three Amazing things that happened today (big or small)?

1) ....

2) ....

3) ....

Projection

My desires/approach for tomorrow:

....

....

....

Date: ___/___/___

Intention:

Today I affirm: ....

Three Things That Would Make Today Great:

1) ....

2) ....

3) ....

Must-do's for the day?

....

....

Mid-Day Check-In

I am grateful for ....

Reflection

Anything about today that I would change?

....

....

....

Three Amazing things that happened today (big or small)?

1) ....

2) ....

3) ....

Projection

My desires/approach for tomorrow:

....

....

....

Date: ___ / ___ / ___

Intention:

Today I affirm:...

Three Things That Would Make Today Great:

1) ....

2) ....

3) ....

Must-do's for the day?

....

....

Mid-Day Check-In

I am grateful for ....

Reflection

Anything about today that I would change?

....

....

....

Three Amazing things that happened today (big or small)?

1) ....

2) ....

3) ....

Projection

My desires/approach for tomorrow:

....

....

....

Date: ___ / ___ / ___

Intention:

Today I affirm:..

Three Things That Would Make Today Great:

1) ....

2) ....

3) ....

Must-do's for the day?

....

....

....

Mid-Day Check-In

I am grateful for ....

Reflection

Anything about today that I would change?

....

....

....

Three Amazing things that happened today (big or small)?

1) ....

2) ....

3) ....

Projection

My desires/approach for tomorrow:

....

....

....

Date: ___ / ___ / ___

Intention:

Today I affirm:...

Three Things That Would Make Today Great:

1) ....

2) ....

3) ....

Must-do's for the day?

....

....

Mid-Day Check-In

I am grateful for ....

Reflection

Anything about today that I would change?

....

....

....

Three Amazing things that happened today (big or small)?

1) ....

2) ....

3) ....

Projection

My desires/approach for tomorrow:

....

....

....

Date: ___/___/___

Intention:

Today I affirm:..

Three Things That Would Make Today Great:

1) ....
2) ....
3) ....

Must-do's for the day?

....

....

Mid-Day Check-In

I am grateful for ....

Reflection

Anything about today that I would change?

....

....

....

Three Amazing things that happened today (big or small)?

1) ....
2) ....
3) ....

Projection

My desires/approach for tomorrow:

....

....

....

Date:___/___/___

Intention:

Today I affirm:...

Three Things That Would Make Today Great:

1) ....

2) ....

3) ....

Must-do's for the day?

....

....

Mid-Day Check-In

I am grateful for ....

Reflection

Anything about today that I would change?

....

....

....

Three Amazing things that happened today (big or small)?

1) ....

2) ....

3) ....

Projection

My desires/approach for tomorrow:

....

....

....

Date: ___ / ___ / ___

Intention:

Today I affirm:..

Three Things That Would Make Today Great:

1) ....

2) ....

3) ....

Must-do's for the day?

....

....

....

Mid-Day Check-In

I am grateful for ....

Reflection

Anything about today that I would change?

....

....

....

Three Amazing things that happened today (big or small)?

1) ....

2) ....

3) ....

Projection

My desires/approach for tomorrow:

....

....

....

Date: ___ / ___ / ___

Intention:

Today I affirm:..

Three Things That Would Make Today Great:

1) ....

2) ....

3) ....

Must-do's for the day?

....

....

....

Mid-Day Check-In

I am grateful for ....

Reflection

Anything about today that I would change?

....

....

....

Three Amazing things that happened today (big or small)?

1) ....

2) ....

3) ....

Projection

My desires/approach for tomorrow:

....

....

....

Date: ___ / ___ / ___

Intention:

Today I affirm: ....

Three Things That Would Make Today Great:

1) ....

2) ....

3) ....

Must-do's for the day?

....

....

Mid-Day Check-In

I am grateful for ....

Reflection

Anything about today that I would change?

....

....

Three Amazing things that happened today (big or small)?

1) ....

2) ....

3) ....

Projection

My desires/approach for tomorrow:

....

....

Date: ___ / ___ / ___

Intention:

Today I affirm:..

Three Things That Would Make Today Great:

1) ....

2) ....

3) ....

Must-do's for the day?

....

....

Mid-Day Check-In

I am grateful for ....

Reflection

Anything about today that I would change?

....

....

Three Amazing things that happened today (big or small)?

1) ....

2) ....

3) ....

Projection

My desires/approach for tomorrow:

....

....

Date:___/___/___

Intention:

Today I affirm:..

Three Things That Would Make Today Great:

1) ....

2) ....

3) ....

Must-do's for the day?

....

....

Mid-Day Check-In

I am grateful for ....

Reflection

Anything about today that I would change?

....

....

Three Amazing things that happened today (big or small)?

1) ....

2) ....

3) ....

Projection

My desires/approach for tomorrow:

....

....

Date: ___/___/___

Intention:

Today I affirm:...

Three Things That Would Make Today Great:

1) ....

2) ....

3) ....

Must-do's for the day?

....

....

....

Mid-Day Check-In

I am grateful for ....

Reflection

Anything about today that I would change?

....

....

....

Three Amazing things that happened today (big or small)?

1) ....

2) ....

3) ....

Projection

My desires/approach for tomorrow:

....

....

....

Date: ___/___/___

Intention:

Today I affirm:..

Three Things That Would Make Today Great:

1) ....

2) ....

3) ....

Must-do's for the day?

....

....

....

Mid-Day Check-In

I am grateful for ....

Reflection

Anything about today that I would change?

....

....

....

Three Amazing things that happened today (big or small)?

1) ....

2) ....

3) ....

Projection

My desires/approach for tomorrow:

....

....

....

Date:_____/_____/_____

Intention:

Today I affirm:...

Three Things That Would Make Today Great:

1) ....

2) ....

3) ....

Must-do's for the day?

....

....

Mid-Day Check-In

I am grateful for ....

Reflection

Anything about today that I would change?

....

....

....

Three Amazing things that happened today (big or small)?

1) ....

2) ....

3) ....

Projection

My desires/approach for tomorrow:

....

....

....

Date: ___ / ___ / ___

Intention:

Today I affirm:...

Three Things That Would Make Today Great:

1) ....

2) ....

3) ....

Must-do's for the day?

....

....

Mid-Day Check-In

I am grateful for ....

Reflection

Anything about today that I would change?

....

....

Three Amazing things that happened today (big or small)?

1) ....

2) ....

3) ....

Projection

My desires/approach for tomorrow:

....

....

....

Date: ___ / ___ / ___

Intention:

Today I affirm:...

Three Things That Would Make Today Great:

1) ....

2) ....

3) ....

Must-do's for the day?

....

....

Mid-Day Check-In

I am grateful for ....

Reflection

Anything about today that I would change?

....

....

....

Three Amazing things that happened today (big or small)?

1) ....

2) ....

3) ....

Projection

My desires/approach for tomorrow:

....

....

Date: ___/___/___

Intention:

Today I affirm: ....

Three Things That Would Make Today Great:

1) ....

2) ....

3) ....

Must-do's for the day?

....

....

Mid-Day Check-In

I am grateful for ....

Reflection

Anything about today that I would change?

....

....

Three Amazing things that happened today (big or small)?

1) ....

2) ....

3) ....

Projection

My desires/approach for tomorrow:

....

....

Date: ___ / ___ / ___

Intention:

Today I affirm:..

Three Things That Would Make Today Great:

1) ....

2) ....

3) ....

Must-do's for the day?

....

....

Mid-Day Check-In

I am grateful for ....

Reflection

Anything about today that I would change?

....

....

Three Amazing things that happened today (big or small)?

1) ....

2) ....

3) ....

Projection

My desires/approach for tomorrow:

....

....

....

Date: ___/___/___

Intention:

Today I affirm: ....

Three Things That Would Make Today Great:

1) ....

2) ....

3) ....

Must-do's for the day?

....

....

Mid-Day Check-In

I am grateful for ....

Reflection

Anything about today that I would change?

....

....

....

Three Amazing things that happened today (big or small)?

1) ....

2) ....

3) ....

Projection

My desires/approach for tomorrow:

....

....

....

Date: ___/___/___

Intention:

Today I affirm:

1)
2)
3)

Must-do's for the day?

Mid-Day Check-In

I am grateful for

Reflection

Anything about today that I would change?

Three Amazing things that happened today (big or small)?

1)
2)
3)

Projection

My desires/approach for tomorrow:

Date: ___ / ___ / ___

Intention:

Today I affirm:...

Three Things That Would Make Today Great:

1) ....

2) ....

3) ....

Must-do's for the day?

....

....

Mid-Day Check-In

I am grateful for ....

Reflection

Anything about today that I would change?

....

....

....

Three Amazing things that happened today (big or small)?

1) ....

2) ....

3) ....

Projection

My desires/approach for tomorrow:

....

....

....

Date: ___/___/___

Intention:

Today I affirm: ....

Three Things That Would Make Today Great:

1) ....

2) ....

3) ....

Must-do's for the day?

....

....

Mid-Day Check-In

I am grateful for ....

Reflection

Anything about today that I would change?

....

....

Three Amazing things that happened today (big or small)?

1) ....

2) ....

3) ....

Projection

My desires/approach for tomorrow:

....

....

....

Date: ___/___/___

Intention:

Today I affirm:..

Three Things That Would Make Today Great:

1) ....

2) ....

3) ....

Must-do's for the day?

....

....

Mid-Day Check-In

I am grateful for ....

Reflection

Anything about today that I would change?

....

....

Three Amazing things that happened today (big or small)?

1) ....

2) ....

3) ....

Projection

My desires/approach for tomorrow:

....

....

....

Date: ___ / ___ / ___

Intention:

Today I affirm: ....

Three Things That Would Make Today Great:

1) ....

2) ....

3) ....

Must-do's for the day?

....

....

....

Mid-Day Check-In

I am grateful for ....

Reflection

Anything about today that I would change?

....

....

....

Three Amazing things that happened today (big or small)?

1) ....

2) ....

3) ....

Projection

My desires/approach for tomorrow:

....

....

....

Date: ___ / ___ / ___

Intention:

Today I affirm:...

Three Things That Would Make Today Great:

1) ....

2) ....

3) ....

Must-do's for the day?

....

....

Mid-Day Check-In

I am grateful for ....

Reflection

Anything about today that I would change?

....

....

....

Three Amazing things that happened today (big or small)?

1) ....

2) ....

3) ....

Projection

My desires/approach for tomorrow:

....

....

....

Date: ___ / ___ / ___

Intention:

Today I affirm: ....

Three Things That Would Make Today Great:

1) ....

2) ....

3) ....

Must-do's for the day?

....

....

....

Mid-Day Check-In

I am grateful for ....

Reflection

Anything about today that I would change?

....

....

....

Three Amazing things that happened today (big or small)?

1) ....

2) ....

3) ....

Projection

My desires/approach for tomorrow:

....

....

....

Date:___/___/___

Intention:

Today I affirm:...

Three Things That Would Make Today Great:

1) ....

2) ....

3) ....

Must-do's for the day?

....

....

Mid-Day Check-In

I am grateful for ....

Reflection

Anything about today that I would change?

....

....

Three Amazing things that happened today (big or small)?

1) ....

2) ....

3) ....

Projection

My desires/approach for tomorrow:

....

....

....

Date:___/___/___

Intention:

Today I affirm:...

1) ....

2) ....

3) ....

Must-do's for the day?

....

....

....

Mid-Day Check-In

I am grateful for ....

Reflection

Anything about today that I would change?

....

....

....

Three Amazing things that happened today (big or small)?

1) ....

2) ....

3) ....

Projection

My desires/approach for tomorrow:

....

....

....

Date: _____/_____/_____

Intention:

Today I affirm:...

Three Things That Would Make Today Great:

1) ....

2) ....

3) ....

Must-do's for the day?

....

....

Mid-Day Check-In

I am grateful for ....

Reflection

Anything about today that I would change?

....

....

Three Amazing things that happened today (big or small)?

1) ....

2) ....

3) ....

Projection

My desires/approach for tomorrow:

....

....

Date:_____/_____/_____

Intention:

Today I affirm:..

Three Things That Would Make Today Great:

1) ....

2) ....

3) ....

Must-do's for the day?

....

....

Mid-Day Check-In

I am grateful for ....

Reflection

Anything about today that I would change?

....

....

....

Three Amazing things that happened today (big or small)?

1) ....

2) ....

3) ....

Projection

My desires/approach for tomorrow:

....

....

....

Date: ___/___/___

Intention:

Today I affirm:..

Three Things That Would Make Today Great:

1) ....

2) ....

3) ....

Must-do's for the day?

....

....

Mid-Day Check-In

I am grateful for ....

Reflection

Anything about today that I would change?

....

....

Three Amazing things that happened today (big or small)?

1) ....

2) ....

3) ....

Projection

My desires/approach for tomorrow:

....

....

Date: ___ / ___ / ___

Intention:

Today I affirm: ....

Three Things That Would Make Today Great:

1) ....

2) ....

3) ....

Must-do's for the day?

....

....

Mid-Day Check-In

I am grateful for ....

Reflection

Anything about today that I would change?

....

....

....

Three Amazing things that happened today (big or small)?

1) ....

2) ....

3) ....

Projection

My desires/approach for tomorrow:

....

....

....

Date: ___/___/___

Intention:

Today I affirm:..

Three Things That Would Make Today Great:

1) ....

2) ....

3) ....

Must-do's for the day?

....

....

....

Mid-Day Check-In

I am grateful for ....

Reflection

Anything about today that I would change?

....

....

....

Three Amazing things that happened today (big or small)?

1) ....

2) ....

3) ....

Projection

My desires/approach for tomorrow:

....

....

....

Date: ___ / ___ / ___

Intention:

Today I affirm: ....

Three Things That Would Make Today Great:

1) ....

2) ....

3) ....

Must-do's for the day?

....

....

Mid-Day Check-In

I am grateful for ....

Reflection

Anything about today that I would change?

....

....

....

Three Amazing things that happened today (big or small)?

1) ....

2) ....

3) ....

Projection

My desires/approach for tomorrow:

....

....

....

Date: ___ / ___ / ___

Intention:

Today I affirm:..

Three Things That Would Make Today Great:

1) ....

2) ....

3) ....

Must-do's for the day?

....

....

....

Mid-Day Check-In

I am grateful for ....

Reflection

Anything about today that I would change?

....

....

....

Three Amazing things that happened today (big or small)?

1) ....

2) ....

3) ....

Projection

My desires/approach for tomorrow:

....

....

....

Date:_____ / _____ / _____

Intention:

Today I affirm:..

Three Things That Would Make Today Great:

1) ....

2) ....

3) ....

Must-do's for the day?

....

....

....

Mid-Day Check-In

I am grateful for ....

Reflection

Anything about today that I would change?

....

....

....

Three Amazing things that happened today (big or small)?

1) ....

2) ....

3) ....

Projection

My desires/approach for tomorrow:

....

....

....

Date: ___/___/___

Intention:

Today I affirm:..

Three Things That Would Make Today Great:

1) ....

2) ....

3) ....

Must-do's for the day?

....

....

Mid-Day Check-In

I am grateful for ....

Reflection

Anything about today that I would change?

....

....

....

Three Amazing things that happened today (big or small)?

1) ....

2) ....

3) ....

Projection

My desires/approach for tomorrow:

....

....

....

Date: ___/___/___

Intention:

Today I affirm:...

Three Things That Would Make Today Great:

1) ....

2) ....

3) ....

Must-do's for the day?

....

....

Mid-Day Check-In

I am grateful for ....

Reflection

Anything about today that I would change?

....

....

....

Three Amazing things that happened today (big or small)?

1) ....

2) ....

3) ....

Projection

My desires/approach for tomorrow:

....

....

....

Date: ___ / ___ / ___

Intention:

Today I affirm:..

Three Things That Would Make Today Great:

1) ....

2) ....

3) ....

Must-do's for the day?

....

....

....

Mid-Day Check-In

I am grateful for ....

Reflection

Anything about today that I would change?

....

....

....

Three Amazing things that happened today (big or small)?

1) ....

2) ....

3) ....

Projection

My desires/approach for tomorrow:

....

....

....

Date:_____/_____/_____

Intention:

Today I affirm:...

Three Things That Would Make Today Great:

1) ....

2) ....

3) ....

Must-do's for the day?

....

....

Mid-Day Check-In

I am grateful for ....

Reflection

Anything about today that I would change?

....

....

....

Three Amazing things that happened today (big or small)?

1) ....

2) ....

3) ....

Projection

My desires/approach for tomorrow:

....

....

....

Date: ___ / ___ / ___

Intention:

Today I affirm:..

Three Things That Would Make Today Great:

1) ....

2) ....

3) ....

Must-do's for the day?

....

....

....

Mid-Day Check-In

I am grateful for ....

Reflection

Anything about today that I would change?

....

....

....

Three Amazing things that happened today (big or small)?

1) ....

2) ....

3) ....

Projection

My desires/approach for tomorrow:

....

....

....

Date: ___ / ___ / ___

Intention:

Today I affirm: ....

Three Things That Would Make Today Great:

1) ....

2) ....

3) ....

Must-do's for the day?

....

....

....

Mid-Day Check-In

I am grateful for ....

Reflection

Anything about today that I would change?

....

....

....

Three Amazing things that happened today (big or small)?

1) ....

2) ....

3) ....

Projection

My desires/approach for tomorrow:

....

....

....

Date:_____/_____/_____

Intention:

Today I affirm:..

Three Things That Would Make Today Great:

1) ....

2) ....

3) ....

Must-do's for the day?

....

....

Mid-Day Check-In

I am grateful for ....

Reflection

Anything about today that I would change?

....

....

....

Three Amazing things that happened today (big or small)?

1) ....

2) ....

3) ....

Projection

My desires/approach for tomorrow:

....

....

....

Date:_____/_____/_____

Intention:

Today I affirm:...

Three Things That Would Make Today Great:

1) ....

2) ....

3) ....

Must-do's for the day?

....

....

Mid-Day Check-In

I am grateful for ....

Reflection

Anything about today that I would change?

....

....

....

Three Amazing things that happened today (big or small)?

1) ....

2) ....

3) ....

Projection

My desires/approach for tomorrow:

....

....

....

Date: ___ / ___ / ___

Intention:

Today I affirm:...

Three Things That Would Make Today Great:

1) ....

2) ....

3) ....

Must-do's for the day?

....

....

....

Mid-Day Check-In

I am grateful for ....

Reflection

Anything about today that I would change?

....

....

....

Three Amazing things that happened today (big or small)?

1) ....

2) ....

3) ....

Projection

My desires/approach for tomorrow:

....

....

....

Date: ___/___/___

Intention:

Today I affirm:..

Three Things That Would Make Today Great:

1) ....

2) ....

3) ....

Must-do's for the day?

....

....

....

Mid-Day Check-In

I am grateful for ....

Reflection

Anything about today that I would change?

....

....

....

Three Amazing things that happened today (big or small)?

1) ....

2) ....

3) ....

Projection

My desires/approach for tomorrow:

....

....

....

Date: ___ / ___ / ___

Intention:

Today I affirm: ....

Three Things That Would Make Today Great:

1) ....

2) ....

3) ....

Must-do's for the day?

....

....

Mid-Day Check-In

I am grateful for ....

Reflection

Anything about today that I would change?

....

....

Three Amazing things that happened today (big or small)?

1) ....

2) ....

3) ....

Projection

My desires/approach for tomorrow:

....

....

Made in the USA
Columbia, SC
12 March 2021